General
Knowledge
Quiz
Time

CHEMISTRY

PHYSICS

LITERATURE

WORLD RELIGIONS

Quiz Time: General Knowledge
Questions & Answers - #4

ISBN - 81-8388-246-3

Published in 2016 by
SPIDER BOOKS
Plot No.1352, 19th Main Road
Anna Nagar(W), Chennai - 600 040. (INDIA)
Phones: 044-42171047 / 42171048
E-mail: spider@spiderbooks.net

Edited by
M.K. Parthasarathy

Disclaimer:
Every effort has been made to ensure that the
entries in this book are correct. The Publisher is
not responsible for any factual or typographical
error which may be found in this book.

Printed in India

CHEMISTRY

1) What is the study of carbon compounds known as?
   - (A) Inorganic Chemistry
   - (B) Organic Chemistry
   - (C) Physical Chemistry
   - (D) Biochemistry

2) What is the melting point or freezing point of water?
   - (A) -32°C
   - (B) 0°C
   - (C) 32°C
   - (D) 96.4°F

3) What does 'N' stand for in DNAs & RNAs?
   - (A) Neutral
   - (B) Nitric
   - (C) Nitrite
   - (D) Nucleic

4) Which of these gas is also called as 'Laughing gas'?
   - (A) Nitrous oxide
   - (B) Di-nitrogen monoxide
   - (C) Both of above
   - (D) None of these

5) Which is the only substance to exist naturally on the earth in all three states - gas, liquid & solid?
   - (A) Oxygen
   - (B) Carbon dioxide
   - (C) Mercury
   - (D) Water

6) Which was the first synthetic plastic in the world?
   - (A) Poly-vinyl chloride
   - (B) Polypropylene
   - (C) Bakelite
   - (D) Polyester

7) Which is the basic unit of all states of matter?
   - (A) Atom
   - (B) Molecule
   - (C) Nucleus
   - (D) Mass

8) Which is a positively charged particle forming part of the atomic nucleus?
   - (A) Proton
   - (B) Electron
   - (C) Neutron
   - (D) Neuron

9) Which is an extremely strong, flexible, fire-resistant polymer with low density, used to make bulletproof vests?

A. Teflon
B. Kevlar
C. Rayon
D. Netlon

10) How many elements are estimated to occur naturally on the earth?

A. 68
B. 75
C. 92
D. 109

11) What is the common element found in charcoal, coal, granite & diamond?

A. Iron
B. Carbon
C. Nitrogen
D. Chromium

12) How a toxic substance like carbon monoxide (CO) emitted by motor vehicles on roads does not harm lives immediately?

A. Get oxidized by air
B. Turning into CO_2
C. Warming globe
D. All of these

13) Which state of matter has a definite shape because their molecules are tightly packed?

A. Gas
B. Liquid
C. Solid
D. All of these

14) What is the process of heating up liquid into gas called as?

A. Condensation
B. Evaporation
C. Conservation
D. Liquefaction

15) Which group of a periodic table has the most number of elements?

A. Lanthanides
B. Actinides
C. Transition metals
D. Inner-transition metals

16) How a compound of an acid & base is called?

(A) Mixture   (B) Solution
(C) Salt   (D) Catalyst

17) Which substance can easily change from solid or liquid state to vapour is known as?

(A) Volatile   (B) Ductile
(C) Fragile   (D) Toxic

18) Which radioactive element is the major source of nuclear energy?

(A) Uranium   (B) Thorium
(C) Plutonium   (D) Cranium

19) Which compound with large modules, composed of many simpler molecules are known as?

(A) Isomers   (B) Polymers
(C) Esters   (D) Alkanes

20) Gun metal is an alloy of how many per cent of Copper, Tin and Zinc in proportion?

(A) 20:50:30   (B) 70:28:2
(C) 88:10:2   (D) 80:12:8

21) Which among these is also known as 'Dry ice'?

(A) Solid carbon dioxide (CO_2)   (B) Solid carbon monoxide (CO)
(C) Liquid oxygen   (D) Solid carbon

22) What is the time during a radioactive decay in which the strength of a radioactive source decays to half its original value called?

(A) Half-time   (B) Half-life
(C) Half-value   (D) Half-strength

23) What is the simplest phenol, known as phenol derived from benzene commonly known as?

(A) Carbonic acid   (B) Carbolic acid

(C) Carboxylic acid   (D) Caproic acid

24) What does pH an acidity - measuring scale refers to?

(A) Part of hydrogen   (B) Position of hydrogen

(C) Potential of hydrogen   (D) Power of hydrogen

25) Which of these is a slow reaction that takes some days?

(A) Chemical reaction   (B) Combustion reaction

(C) Volatile reaction   (D) Corrosive reaction

26) Which natural element has the highest melting point of 3400°C?

(A) Gold   (B) Platinum

(C) Iron   (D) Tungsten

27) What is the oxidation of metals by burning in air called as?

(A) Sublimation   (B) Condensation

(C) Calcination   (D) Coronation

28) What substance is added in small quantities to the water supplies, to prevent tooth decay?

(A) Fluoride   (B) Bromide

(C) Iodide   (D) Chloride

29) What is the naturally occurring mineral known as?

(A) Ore   (B) Metal

(C) Substance   (D) Metalloid

30) What are the radioactive elements called as?

(A) Transition elements   (B) Transuranic elements

(C) Lanthanides   (D) Actinides

31) Which is a lighter, non-flammable gas used in balloons & airships?

A Hydrogen
B Helium
C Argon
D Xenon

32) What is the name for hydride of nitrogen (NH₃)?

A Hydro nitrogen
B Nitrogen hydroxide
C Ammonia
D Nitrogen peroxide

33) Which is the rarely available element on the earth's surface?

A Thorium
B Bismuth
C Astatine
D Vanadium

34) Which was used as a local anaesthetic & an early ingredient in Coca-cola?

A Cocaine
B Codeine
C Caffeine
D Nicotine

35) What attributes to repetition of short circuit if an electric fire is doused with –

A Sand
B Water
C Carbon dioxide
D All of these

36) Which is a toxic substance in a leaded petrol, which can cause brain damage specially in children?

A Carbon
B Hydrogen
C Sulphur
D Tetraethyl Lead

37) Which glass is used to make oven-ware & laboratory glassware?

A Soda lime glass
B Lead glass
C Borosilicate glass
D Float glass

38) How many elements are named after the Universal planets including Pluto?

A 2
B 3
C 4
D 6

39) Which chemical is used to preserve food grains?

(A) Potassium permanganate   (B) Sodium benzoate
(C) Borax   (D) Sodium silicate

40) Which metal is a liquid at room temperature, used in thermometers?

(A) Sodium   (B) Potassium
(C) Mercury   (D) Magnesium

41) What are aerosols mostly made up of?

(A) DNAs   (B) BCGs
(C) TNTs   (D) CFCs

42) Prolonged inhalation of what causes the Lung cancer?

(A) Sulphur dioxide   (B) Carbon monoxide
(C) Asbestos   (D) Sodium hydroxide

43) What is the combination of two or more metals known as?

(A) Alkali   (B) Alkaloid
(C) Alloy   (D) Alumina

44) What does the acronym 'CFC' refer to?

(A) Carbon forming chemical   (B) Carbon fuel chemical
(C) Chlorofluorocarbon   (D) Carbon fluoro chloride

45) Which is the costlier metal among these?

(A) Platinum   (B) Gold
(C) Titanium   (D) Iridium

46) What is the term for oil, straight from an oil well is called?

(A) Petroleum   (B) Crude oil
(C) Hydrocarbons   (D) Alkanes

47) Deuterium & Tritium are the isotopes of which gaseous element?

(A) Hydrogen
(B) Helium
(C) Argon
(D) Neon

48) Which of these fruits does not contain citric acid?

(A) Lemon
(B) Sweet lime
(C) Pineapple
(D) Mango

49) The deficiency of what causes dehydration?

(A) Hydrogen
(B) Oxygen
(C) Water
(D) Salt

50) What is the main component of a glass?

(A) Calcium
(B) Coal
(C) Carbon
(D) Sand (Silica)

51) Which is not a halogen - an extreme form of the non-metals among these?

(A) Chlorine
(B) Bromine
(C) Astatine
(D) Sulphur

52) A substance that reacts with a base to form salt & water is called as –

(A) Compound
(B) Acid
(C) Element
(D) Mixture

53) What is the pH value of an acidic solution at 25°C?

(A) Less than 7.0
(B) Less than 5.0
(C) 7.0
(D) More than 7.0

54) Which is the parent material of stainless steel?

(A) Iron
(B) Nickel
(C) Chromium
(D) Carbon

55) When an ice in a beaker of water melts, the water level will –

(A) Increase
(B) Decrease
(C) Vanish
(D) Remain the same

56) The smallest unit of a substance that retains all the properties of that substance is called –

(A) Molecule
(B) Nucleus
(C) Electron
(D) Neutron

57) What are the dispersion of a solid or liquid in a gas like smoke & fog?

(A) Aerogels
(B) Aerosols
(C) Aerofoils
(D) Aerophytes

58) Which is an insulator, but a good conductor of heat used in electric iron box?

(A) Iron
(B) Nickel
(C) Chromium
(D) Mica

59) What is the lowest possible temperature theoretically, also called 'absolute zero' at which molecules become motionless?

(A) -273.15°C
(B) -459.67°F
(C) Both of above
(D) None of these

60) The boiling point of sea water is more than that of pure water because of –

(A) Salt content
(B) Impurities
(C) Salinity
(D) All of these

61) Which is the hardest among all other substances on the earth with a Mohr's scale of 10?

(A) Diamond
(B) Carborundum
(C) Corundum
(D) Topaz

62) A solid changes directly to a gaseous state without passing through liquid state is called –

- (A) Condensation
- (B) Sublimation
- (C) Liquefaction
- (D) Liquidation

63) Any medical treatment with synthetic chemicals against infectious disease is known as –

- (A) Haemotherapy
- (B) Chemotherapy
- (C) Aromatherapy
- (D) Hydrotherapy

64) What will be the temperature of a boiling water in a vessel or any container?

- (A) 100°C
- (B) More than 100°C
- (C) 120°C
- (D) None of these

65) Which is also known as 'Milk of Magnesia' used as an antacid to neutralize the stomach acids?

- (A) Magnesium chloride
- (B) Magnesium sulphate
- (C) Magnesium carbonate
- (D) Magnesium hydroxide

66) What is the name of an alloy of Mercury with other metals?

- (A) Amalgol
- (B) Amalgam
- (C) Amatol
- (D) Amagol

67) What is the major content of the cereals of about 75%?

- (A) Proteins
- (B) Fats
- (C) Vitamins
- (D) Carbohydrates

68) What is a foreign substance in a chemical reaction which alters the rate of reaction without undergoing any change in itself?

- (A) Catalyst
- (B) Amethyst
- (C) Chemocyst
- (D) Haemocyst

69) Which is the raw material to produce safety matches?

A) Red phosphorus
B) White phosphorus
C) Potassium nitrate
D) Sodium nitrate

70) Which is the heaviest element of all at 22.59 gm/cu.cm at 20°C?

A) Osmium
B) Iridium
C) Platinum
D) Chromium

71) Which is the cheapest commercial acid among these?

A) Sulphuric acid
B) Nitric acid
C) Hydrochloric acid
D) Mallic acid

72) What is the common name for acetaldehyde (CH_3CHO)?

A) Ethanal
B) Ethanol
C) Ethyl alcohol
D) All of these

73) Which is not a type of metal-extracting process?

A) Pyrometallurgy
B) Hydrometallurgy
C) Gyrometallurgy
D) None of these

74) Gunpowder is a mixture of which two fuels with an oxidant-potassium nitrate?

A) Carbon & Oxygen
B) Carbon & Sulphur
C) Carbon & Hydrogen
D) Sulphur & Hydrogen

75) What is the term of water vapour present in the atmospheric air known as –

A) Moisture
B) Humidity
C) Perspiration
D) Liquidation

76) Which of these alloys is used for making magnets?

A) Duralumin
B) Alnico
C) Gunmetal
D) Bell metal

77) Which of these elements is obtained from seaweeds?

(A) Magnesium   (B) Sulphur
(C) Vanadium   (D) Molybdenum

78) Which was the first element recognized & experimented to have radioactive properties?

(A) Plutonium   (B) Polonium
(C) Uranium   (D) Thorium

79) The elementary particle which is the fundamental constituent of all hadrons is called –

(A) Quart   (B) Quartz
(C) Quark   (D) Quarkz

80) The total number of protons & neutrons in an atom is called its –

(A) Atomic number   (B) Atomic weight
(C) Mass number   (D) All of these

81) Which uranium isotope or form is used as a fuel in nuclear reactors to produce electrical energy?

(A) U^{233} (B) U^{235}
(C) U^{238} (D) All of these

82) What gas is used in carbonated drinks such as soft drinks, sodas & lemonades?

(A) Carbon monoxide   (B) Carbon dioxide
(C) Liquid oxygen   (D) Solid carbon dioxide

83) What are normally the sweet smelling compounds found in perfumes & in fruit flavours?

(A) Alkanes   (B) Alkenes
(C) Esters   (D) Ethers

84) What are the chemical messengers carried round the body in the blood stream called?

A) Glands
B) Hormones
C) Lipids
D) Vitamins

85) Which of these fibres is least prone to fire?

A) Nylon
B) Cotton
C) Rayon
D) Terry cott

86) What are biological compounds which are soluble in organic solvents but insoluble in water?

A) Proteins
B) Vitamins
C) Fats
D) Lipids

87) The element with properties which are in between those of metals & non-metals called –

A) Alloy
B) Isotope
C) Metalloid
D) Alkaloid

88) Which is a narcotic drug obtained from opium, used in cough mixture?

A) Codeine
B) Caffeine
C) Carotene
D) Coffin

89) What is a product formulated to protect & decorate surfaces, has three ingredients - pigments, polymers & a solvent?

A) Paint
B) Varnish
C) Acrylic paste
D) Distemper

90) Which among these is the richest source for vitamin A?

A) Carrot
B) Milk
C) Egg
D) All of these

91) Which is used as an antifreeze in automobile engines?

(A) Methanol
(B) Ethanol
(C) Propyl alcohol
(D) Ethylene Glycol

92) What acid is present in vitamin C?

(A) Citric acid
(B) Lactic acid
(C) Folic acid
(D) Ascorbic acid

93) What are the different forms of the same element however, in the same physical state known as?

(A) Allotropic form
(B) Amorphous form
(C) Heterogeneous form
(D) Homogenous form

94) What are the compounds of carbon, hydrogen & oxygen called?

(A) Aldehydes
(B) Alcohols
(C) Carbohydrates
(D) Hydrocarbons

95) What chemical is given to those subjected to a Narco-analysis test (lie test) which induces a hypnotic state to tell the truth?

(A) Sodium propionate
(B) Sodium pentothal
(C) Sodium glutamate
(D) Sodium bi-carbonate

96) Which is an endothermic reaction in which the energy is taken from their surroundings?

(A) Condensation
(B) Evaporation
(C) Freezing
(D) All of these

97) What is a process of obtaining pure water from seawater or other sources of water called?

(A) Salination
(B) Desalination
(C) Distillation
(D) Crystallization

98) Excessive consumption of what may cause a disaster called 'Chinese restaurant syndrome'?

(A) Mono-sodium Glutamate
(B) MSG
(C) Vestin
(D) All of these

99) What are the open chain organic compounds called as?

(A) Allopatric
(B) Aliphatic
(C) Alicyclic
(D) Aromatic

100) What are cocaine, morphine, caffeine, strychnine, the types of?

(A) Alkaloid
(B) Alkane
(C) Alkene
(D) Alkanal

101) Which of these has the highest rate of fuel values?

(A) Petrol
(B) Coal
(C) Natural gas
(D) Hydrogen

102) Which among these is highly flammable & has to be stored under water or otherwise catches fire in air?

(A) White phosphorus
(B) Red phosphorus
(C) Black phosphorus
(D) All of these

103) What is the common name of mineral with mercury sulphide?

(A) Mennabar
(B) Nannabar
(C) Cinnabar
(D) Milkybar

104) Which is the lightest element of 0.553 gm/cu.cm. – 42 times lighter than the heaviest osmium?

(A) Helium
(B) Lithium
(C) Potassium
(D) Sodium

105) Which is the highly poisonous extract of 'opium'?

A) Thebaine
B) Codeine
C) Morphine
D) Di-morphine

106) What was hydrochloric acid (Hcl) formerly known as?

A) Solution of salts
B) Spirits of salts
C) Chloro salts
D) Hydro salts

107) Which Halide is a non-metallic element occur in liquid form?

A) Iodine
B) Fluorine
C) Astatine
D) Bromine

108) Which is used as local anaesthetic, makes a specific part of the body numb?

A) Barbiturate
B) Hallothene
C) Lignocaine
D) All of these

109) Which is the substitute for costly radium, a radioactive isotope used in cancer therapy?

A) Iodine-131
B) Bismuth-209
C) Cobalt-60
D) All of these

110) Which is the common element present in all acids?

A) Oxygen
B) Hydrogen
C) Carbon
D) Nitrogen

111) Cooking gas LPG is a mixture of what?

A) Butane & methane
B) Butane & propane
C) Propane & methane
D) Butane & ethane

112) Which is a synthetic radioactive metallic element provide powers to the orbiting satellites?

A) Radium
B) Curium
C) Cerium
D) Polonium

113) What material is used in display devices of a digital watch or a television?

(A) Neon gas   (B) Argon gas
(C) Sodium vapour   (D) Liquid crystal

114) What gas was leaked from Union Carbide's factory in Bhopal gas tragedy?

(A) Phenyl isocyanate   (B) Methyl isocyanate
(C) Ethyl cyanide   (D) Sodium cyanide

115) What is the ratio of composition of Gunpowder – a mixture of potassium nitrate, charcoal & sulphur?

(A) 50:35:15   (B) 60:25:15
(C) 60:30:10   (D) 75:15:10

116) Which is the lightest metal of all?

(A) Potassium (K)   (B) Lithium (Li)
(C) Cadmium (Cd)   (D) Titanium (Ti)

117) What is the name of an enzyme that breaks down the proteins during digestion?

(A) Pepsin   (B) Pepsi
(C) Coke   (D) Sprite

118) Which element has the largest number of isotopes (27) and 5000 times as radioactive as radium?

(A) Tellurium   (B) Thorium
(C) Polonium   (D) Cerium

119) What is the alternative name for rare-earth elements?

(A) Lanthanides   (B) Actinides
(C) Transactinides   (D) All of these

120) What is the name of plastic explosive, a Czech republic made, safe to handle, smell less & difficult to trace?

| A | Syntax | B | Semtex |
| C | Expotex | D | Nanotex |

121) Which of these fuel is heavier & oilier?

| A | Octane | B | Petrol |
| C | Diesel | D | All of these |

122) Aqua regia-a mixture of fuming, corrosive acids of what, can dissolve almost all metals including gold?

| A | Hcl & H_2SO_4 | B | HNO_3 & H_2SO_4 |
| C | HNO_3 & Hcl | D | All of these |

123) Which is the most commonly used bleaching agent?

| A | Ammonia | B | Chlorine |
| C | Sodium chloride | D | Bromine |

124) Which among these is a common salt we use?

| A | Potassium chloride | B | Sodium chloride |
| C | Calcium chloride | D | Ammonium chloride |

125) Plaster of Paris is made from what among these?

| A | Calcium carbonate | B | Calcium chloride |
| C | Gypsum | D | Limestone |

126) Which metal has the major composition of 88% Gun metal - a type of bronze?

| A | Iron | B | Copper |
| C | Tin | D | Zinc |

127) What is a chemical which fixes a dye to the fibres of a textile called?

A) Oxidant
B) Mordant
C) Dormant
D) Solvent

128) Apart from carbon & Tungsten, which element has the melting point of 3000°C & above?

A) Osmium
B) Tantalum
C) Rhenium
D) Rhodium

129) Which is the most common element other than water (H&O) & common salt (Nacl) in seawater?

A) Calcium
B) Sulphur
C) Magnesium
D) Uranium

130) What is the common name for trichloro methane, a substance used as an anaesthetic & a solvent?

A) Laudanum
B) Chloroform
C) Ester
D) Ether

131) What is the pH value of a strong acid?

A) 1.0
B) 5.0
C) 7.0
D) 14.0

132) What are agrochemicals which kill the living organisms that cause damage to the crops, food, wood, fabrics & other materials called?

A) Insecticides
B) Pesticides
C) Herbicides
D) All of these

133) What type of cells are light in weight, used in mobile phones & notebook computers?

A) Lead-acid cells
B) Nickel-cadmium cells
C) Lithium cells
D) All of these

134) What is the common name for poly tetra fluoroethylene, which is used in non-stick cooking vessels & electric iron boxes?

(A) Teflon   (B) Nylon
(C) Terylene   (D) Tefillin

135) What are the organic compounds formed by the reaction between an alcohol & an acid called?

(A) Alkane   (B) Alkene
(C) Ester   (D) Ethylene

136) What is the active chemical constituent of an analgesic drug 'Aspirin'?

(A) Ascorbic acid   (B) Salicylic acid
(C) Formic acid   (D) Mallic acid

137) Pig iron is obtained by smelting which of these iron ores?

(A) Hematite (Fe_2O_3)   (B) Magnetite (Fe_3O_4)
(C) Siderite (Fe_2Co_3)   (D) All of above

138) What are the three major nutrients needed for plants, supplied through fertilizers?

(A) N-P-K   (B) N-Ca-P
(C) N-P-Na   (D) N-P-Mg

139) What is an oxide of hydrogen also called as?

(A) Hydrogen peroxide   (B) Hydrogen oxide
(C) Water   (D) All of these

140) Which is an aluminium alloy consists of copper, magnesium & manganese, usually used in the construction of aircrafts?

(A) Alum   (B) Alumina
(C) Duralumin   (D) Alunite

PHYSICS

141) Name the study of mechanisms & rates of chemical reactions –

A Dynamics
B Mechanics
C Kinetics
D Statics

142) What is the name of the branch of physics dealing with the production & control of electrons in devices such as semiconductors, vacuum tubes, etc.?

A Thermodynamics
B Electronics
C Heat transfer
D Electromagnetism

143) Which Engine works on an external combustion?

A Diesel Engine
B Jet Engine
C Electric Engine
D Steam Engine

144) Among these which type of radiation is more harmful to humans?

A Alpha Rays
B Gamma Rays
C Beta Rays
D X-Rays

145) What is the study of an object or system that moves?

A Dynamics
B Optics
C Statics
D Kinetics

146) What kind of Energy does water filled in the reservoir of a dam have?

A Kinetic energy
B Potential energy
C Mechanical energy
D Electrical energy

147) What is the curved surface of a liquid in tubes known as?

A Hibiscus
B Meniscus
C Pegasus
D Nemesis

148) What is a branch of physics dealing with the transformation of heat into & from other forms of energy called?

A) Thermo dynamics
B) Kinematics
C) Hydrostatics
D) Freakonomics

149) What is the velocity of a vehicle moving in an atmosphere divided by the velocity of sound in the same region equivalent to 1200Km/hr called?

A) Jumbo mach
B) Jet mach
C) Mach number
D) Super number

150) What is the unit for measuring sounds?

A) Hertz
B) Decibels
C) Faraday
D) Siemens

151) What do you normally use to lubricate a machine?

A) Water
B) Foam
C) Acid
D) Oil (or) Grease

152) What is a positive electrode of an electrolytic cell called?

A) Anode
B) Cathode
C) Diode
D) None of these

153) What instrument is used for measuring electric current?

A) Ammeter
B) Voltmeter
C) Galvanometer
D) Pyrometer

154) Which colour among these is not a primary colour?

A) Red
B) Green
C) Orange
D) Blue

155) What is the unit for describing the temperature inside a star which is approximately one Billion°C for a single unit?

A) Infinum   B) Inferno
C) Influxo   D) Infinito

156) What is the speed of sound in the air?

A) 340 m/sec   B) 340 m/min
C) 340 km/hr   D) 3400 km/hr

157) Which is the major source of energy around the world?

A) Nuclear power   B) Solar power
C) Hydrothermal power   D) Fossil fuels

158) What is the rate of change of distance known as?

A) Time   B) Speed
C) Frequency   D) Volume

159) What among these are the good conductors of Heat & Electricity?

A) Wood   B) Plastics
C) Metals   D) Alkalis

160) At what degrees, Celsius & Fahrenheit read the same?

A) -40⁰   B) 0⁰
C) 32⁰   D) 40⁰

161) What is the speed of light in vacuum?

A) 30000 km/sec   B) 300,000 km/sec
C) 3000 km/hr   D) 300,000 km/hr

162) In which of these state of matter the sound travels fast?

A) Gas   B) Liquid
C) Solid   D) All of these

163) The oil in the wick of an oil lamp rises up due to the –

A Surface tension B Capillary action
C Viscosity of oil D Centrifugal force

164) What is the name of the device for disconnecting rotating shafts, used specially in motor vehicle's transmission system?

A Gear B Clutch
C Choke D Carburettor

165) What produces a narrow beam of light capable of travelling over vast distances without any dispersion?

A Laser B Maser
C Fraser D Naesar

166) Which characteristic feature is common to both cathode rays & X-rays?

A Positively charged B Negatively charged
C Neutral D None of these

167) What is the force exerted on an object by gravity called?

A Mass B Weight
C Volume D All of these

168) What it appears to be when seven spectrum colours are painted evenly on to a disc & the disc spins rapidly?

A Red B Blue
C Green D White

169) Electric power of 1000 watts used in one hour is equivalent to one –

A Kilowatt (kw) B Megawatt (mw)
C Horsepower D All of these

170) What kind of Turbine engines are used to drive ship's propellers?

A	Air Turbines	B	Water Turbines
C	Steam Turbines	D	All of these

171) Thermostat is an instrument to maintain constant of what in a electrical equipment?

A	Pressure	B	Temperature
C	Electric current	D	Electric volt

172) What is the speed of an object in a given direction called?

A	Force	B	Velocity
C	Frequency	D	Intensity

173) What is the minimum speed to escape the earth's gravitational pull called 'escape velocity'?

A	11.2 km/sec	B	672 km/min
C	40320 km/hr	D	All of these

174) What is the science of friction, lubrication & lubricants called?

A	Lubriology	B	Frictology
C	Tribology	D	Saibology

175) What number is used to indicate the flow of fluid through a pipe or around an obstruction called?

A	Reynolds number	B	Parker's number
C	Avogadro's number	D	Pythagoras number

176) What is a branch of physics that deals with the study of Light & Vision called?

A	Optics	B	Ophthalmology
C	Optometrics	D	All of these

177) Which form of energy is produced by the motion of molecules?

A	Light	B	Heat
C	Electric	D	All of these

178) Which is a bad conductor of heat filled inside the double walled glass of a Thermos flask?

A	Water	B	Aerosol
C	Wood	D	Air

179) What is a stable particle formed from two protons & two neutrons?

A	Alpha particle	B	Beta particle
C	Atomic particle	D	Sub-atomic particle

180) The weight of a floating body equals to the weight of fluid displaced by it is called –

A	Archimedes' principle	B	Law of floatation
C	Both of above	D	None of these

181) What is the study of communication & automatic control systems in the machines & living things known as?

A	Cryogenics	B	Cybernetics
C	Eugenics	D	Kinematics

182) With reference to motor vehicles, what do the letters 'CC' represent?

A	Cubic Center	B	Cubic Centimeter
C	Cubic Capacity	D	Cubic Captivity

183) Which among these is not a form of mechanical energy?

A	Potential energy	B	Kinetic energy
C	Mass energy	D	Electric energy

184) Which control changes the level of noise produced on a music system?

(A) Tone	(B) Volume
(C) Bass	(D) Treble

185) Which among these is a non-renewable resource of energy?

(A) Wind power	(B) Hydropower
(C) Solar power	(D) Oil (fuels)

186) How a radiator is helpful to an automobile's engine?

(A) By starting	(B) By working
(C) By cooling	(D) By conditioning

187) What is 'Otto Cycle' - used by many internal combustion engines & also diesel engines?

(A) 2-stroke cycle	(B) 3-stroke cycle
(C) 4-stroke cycle	(D) All of these

188) What is the logical basis in the Celsius (ºC) scale?

(A) Freezing point of water	(B) Melting point of water
(C) Boiling point of water	(D) All of these

189) Which among these uses the reflected radio waves to determine the presence, location & speed of distance objects?

(A) Sonar	(B) Solar
(C) Radar	(D) All of these

190) Which among these expands the most when heated?

(A) Gas	(B) Liquid
(C) Solid	(D) All of these

191) The term 'Light Year' is associated with which among these?

(A) Time	(B) Speed
(C) Velocity	(D) Distance

192) Which instrument is used to measure the blood pressure of a man?

(A) Lactometer	(B) Sphygmomanometer
(C) Thermometer	(D) Stethoscope

193) What is the reduced weight of a man or any object on the moon where the gravity is less compared to the earth's?

(A) One-third	(B) One-fourth
(C) One-fifth	(D) One-sixth

194) A wire with high resistance & low melting point is used in –

(A) Fuses	(B) Transformers
(C) Circuit breakers	(D) All of these

195) What is a temperature controlling device that makes use of a feedback & work accordingly to it?

(A) Thermograph	(B) Thermoplast
(C) Thermometer	(D) Thermostat

196) What is the term for the rate at which the velocity of an object changes?

(A) Displacement	(B) Relative motion
(C) Acceleration	(D) Vibration

197) Which telescope comprises of both, lenses & mirrors?

(A) Reflecting telescope	(B) Refracting telescope
(C) Catadioptric telescope	(D) All of these

198) What instrument is used to study the composition of light emitted by a source?

A) Optometer	B) Spectrometer
C) Chronometer	D) Spygometer

199) The force acting normally onto a body per unit surface area is known as–

A) Volume	B) Motion
C) Pressure	D) Mass

200) What is an agreed amount of physical quantity used to express the result of a measurement called?

A) Volume	B) Time
C) Speed	D) Unit

201) What is the deviation between the erroneous result of a measurement and the true value called?

A) Fault	B) Foul
C) Error	D) Wrong

202) What is the device for transforming mechanical energy into electrical energy by means of a coil rotating in a magnetic field called?

A) Accumulator	B) Generator
C) Magnetron	D) Rotator

203) What is the mutual attraction between any two masses in the universe called?

A) Magnetism	B) Gravitation
C) Drawing	D) Pulling

204) What is the method of producing 3D images by means of laser light known as?

A) Polaroid	B) Laseroid
C) Holography	D) Logography

205) Which term means faster than the speed of sound?

| A | Stereophonic | B | Stereotypic |
| C | Supersonic | D | Bionic |

206) The electricity generated from the underground heat created by volcanoes are called –

| A | Solar energy | B | Thermal energy |
| C | Geothermal energy | D | Hydroelectric energy |

207) Which light works on the principle of Electric discharge through gases?

| A | Fluorescent lamp | B | Incandescent lamp |
| C | Electric lamp | D | All of these |

208) A dynamo converts mechanical energy into what energy?

| A | Kinetic energy | B | Potential energy |
| C | Electric energy | D | Nuclear energy |

209) When the milk is churned, what force brings the cream above the milk?

| A | Centripetal force | B | Centrifugal force |
| C | Gravitational force | D | Frictional force |

210) What does the acronym 'pixel' in a digital camera refer to?

| A | Photo element | B | Picture element |
| C | Photo elegance | D | Picture elegance |

211) In microwave cooking, microwaves are attracted & absorbed by what, which rotates rapidly, bumps onto each other & cooks (or) heats the food by friction of its molecules?

| A | Water | B | Fat |
| C | Salt & sugar | D | All of these |

212) The 'absolute zero' is the logical basis of which of these temperature scale?

A) Fahrenheit
B) Kelvin
C) Both of above
D) None of these

213) What lens is used for long-sightedness & in rear view mirrors?

A) Concave
B) Convex
C) Both of above
D) None of these

214) What is the name of branch of physics that studies materials & effects at temperature approaching absolute zero?

A) Kyrogenics
B) Cryogenics
C) Cytogenics
D) Eugenics

215) What is the mass per unit volume of a material called?

A) Density
B) Intensity
C) Capacity
D) Acidity

216) A nautical mile (knot) used in Navigation is equivalent to –

A) One km
B) 1.2 km
C) 1.6 km
D) 1.85 km

217) What is the basic unit of electric current of SI system?

A) Watt
B) Volt
C) Ampere
D) Newtons

218) What is the characteristic of an object or substance to return quickly to its original shape & size after being bent, stretched or squashed, known as?

A) Density
B) Tenacity
C) Elasticity
D) Intensity

219) What is the international system (SI) unit of mass (Volume)?

A	Quintal	B	Pound
C	Gallon	D	Kilogram

220) What is the force that causes rotation, twisting or turning on an object called?

A	Torsion	B	Torque
C	Friction	D	Tension

221) What is the study of the action of force on matter called?

A	Motion	B	Mechanics
C	Bionics	D	Diffraction

222) The rate at which work is being done is known as –

A	Force	B	Power
C	Strength	D	Energy

223) The number of cycles per unit time of any event occurs is called –

A	Quantity	B	Thrust
C	Frequency	D	Prevalence

224) What is the name of special instrument used to detect & measure the nuclear radiation & particles?

A	Tachometer	B	Geiger-Muller Counter
C	Galvanometer	D	Van de Graff accelerator

225) In a standing wave, the points of zero oscillation or amplitude is known as –

A	Mode	B	Node
C	Code	D	Rode

226) The resistance offered by an object to a force applied to it is called –

- **A** Susceptibility
- **B** Immunity
- **C** Hostility
- **D** Inertia

227) What is the basic unit of work in the international system (SI) of units?

- **A** Calorie
- **B** Joule
- **C** Newton
- **D** Kelvin

228) The amount of space occupied by an object or system is its –

- **A** Ability
- **B** Extent
- **C** Volume
- **D** Weight

229) What is the change occurs when a system either gains or loses energy through working but not by heating or cooling?

- **A** Acrobatic
- **B** Adiabatic
- **C** Achromatic
- **D** Actinic

230) What is the rate of energy transfer of one joule per second called?

- **A** Volt
- **B** Ohm
- **C** Watt
- **D** Hertz

231) What is the shortest distance along the path of a wave between two points where displacements are changing in phase known as?

- **A** Wave speed
- **B** Wavelength
- **C** Wave motion
- **D** Wave number

232) What is a physical or mathematical quantity, which has both direction & magnitude called?

- **A** Static quantity
- **B** Vector quantity
- **C** Number quantity
- **D** Algebric quantity

233) What is the frictional force, which opposes movement within the fluid called?

| (A) Vitreosity | (B) Viscosity |
| (C) Polarity | (D) Luminosity |

234) What is the sound of high frequency of short wavelength used for non-destructive exploration of the inside of a human body?

| (A) Hyper sound | (B) Ultrasound |
| (C) Super sound | (D) Mega sound |

235) What is a force spread over an area instead of acting through a point of application called?

| (A) Pressure | (B) Thrust |
| (C) Impact | (D) Effort |

236) What is the energy travelling through space in the form of photons called?

| (A) Diffusion | (B) Radiation |
| (C) Refraction | (D) Reflexion |

237) What is the temperature above which it is impossible to liquefy the gas, no matter how great the compression is applied?

| (A) Constant temperature | (B) Critical temperature |
| (C) Extreme temperature | (D) Standard temperature |

238) What is a light given out when crushing or breaking a material called?

| (A) Chemiluminescence | (B) Triboluminescence |
| (C) Phosphorescence | (D) Fluorescence |

239) What is used to reduce friction wherever one surface slides over another in machines?

| (A) Petrol | (B) Diesel |
| (C) Lubricants | (D) Vaseline |

240) What is the amount of matter contained in the body called?

(A) Mass
(B) Bulk
(C) Heap
(D) Horde

241) What is the hand-held survey instrument for measuring angles of slope called?

(A) Compass
(B) Calliper
(C) Clinometer
(D) Tensimeter

242) What is the study of relationship between people, the furniture, tools & machinery they use at work called?

(A) Economics
(B) Freakonomics
(C) Ergonomics
(D) Mechanics

243) The imperial unit horsepower is replaced by what SI unit?

(A) Ampere
(B) Volt
(C) Watt
(D) Ohm

244) What is the science that treats gases in motion known as?

(A) Aeronautics
(B) Acrobatics
(C) Aerodynamics
(D) Aero statics

245) The SI unit of work & energy – Joule (J) is equivalent to how many calories per unit?

(A) 2.4
(B) 3.6
(C) 4.2
(D) 5.6

246) What is the measure of the brightness of star or other celestial objects known as?

(A) Amplitude
(B) Magnitude
(C) Destitude
(D) Altitude

247) What does 'PAL', the coding system for colour TV broadcasting adapted by European country refer to?

A. Power amplification by line
B. Power alternation by line
C. Phase amplification by line
D. Phase alternation by line

248) An elementary particle having the same magnitude of mass & charge as an electron but exhibiting a positive charge is called –

A. Photon
B. Positron
C. Meson
D. Hadron

249) What is the radiation with wavelengths lesser than that of red light but shorter than microwaves called?

A. Ultra violet Rays
B. Infra-red rays
C. Gamma rays
D. Beta rays

250) What is the amount of heat required to raise unit mass (1kg) of a substance by 1°C called?

A. Specific heat capacity
B. Latent heat capacity
C. Surface heat capacity
D. All of these

251) What is the SI unit for Luminous intensity?

A. Farced
B. Siemen
C. Tesla
D. Candela

252) What is the study of sound & sound waves known as?

A. Acoustics
B. Infrasonics
C. Hypersonic
D. Ultrasonic

253) What does 'SEQAM', the coding system for CTV broadcasting used in France & Eastern Europe refer to?

A Sequential & Magnetic   B Sequential & Memory
C Specific & Magnetic   D Specific & Memory

254) What is the point through which the weight of a body acts called?

A Point of gravity   B Centre of gravity
C Force of gravity   D Pressure of gravity

255) An electrical device that converts an alternating current (AC) into a direct current (DC) is known as –

A Alternator   B Rectifier
C Accumulator   D Capacitor

256) What is the energy radiated in the form of pressure waves into the medium surrounding a vibrating body called?

A Wound   B Sound
C Mound   D Pound

257) The change in length or volume of a body subjected to stress, divided by the original length or volume is called –

A Vain   B Pain
C Strain   D Drain

258) An electrical device that alters the voltage of an AC (alternating current) is –

A Transporter   B Transformer
C Translator   D Transverser

259) Which instrument measures extremely high temperatures?

| A | Thermometer | B | Pyrometer |
| C | Hygrometer | D | Hydrometer |

260) A state of matter achieved at very high temperature in which all the atoms in a gas form positive ions & free electrons known as –

| A | Gel | B | Colloid |
| C | Plasma | D | Foam |

261) Which instrument is used for measuring the atmospheric pressure at any place?

| A | Barometer | B | Anemometer |
| C | Pyrometer | D | Gyrometer |

262) Which instrument can detect, compare or measure low voltage?

| A | Barometer | B | Sonometer |
| C | Galvanometer | D | Gyrometer |

263) What is the substance that does not conduct either heat or electricity?

| A | Inductor | B | Indictor |
| C | Insulator | D | Inspirator |

264) The force that has to be overcome to produce work in a system or machine is known as –

| A | Freight | B | Load |
| C | Consignment | D | Shipment |

265) What is the ability of an electric circuit to store charge known as?

| A | Conductance | B | Capacitance |
| C | Buoyance | D | Inductance |

266) An electronic device made of various kinds of semi-conductors that can amplify a current passing through it or switch the current on or off in response to small controlling signal is –

A	Amplifier	B	Transistor
C	Capacitor	D	Semi-conductor

267) The deviation of an image produced by a lens or mirror caused by light rays coming to focus at different positions is called –

A	Abbreviation	B	Aberration
C	Diffraction	D	Deflection

268) The inter-atomic or inter-molecular forces that bind the atoms or molecules of two different materials, placed in contact at the boundary between them is known as –

A	Addison	B	Adhesion
C	Cohesion	D	Collision

269) What are a class of sub-atomic particles consisting of protons, neutrons & hyperons called?

A	Baryons	B	Mesons
C	Hadrons	D	All of these

270) The movement of molecules from a surrounding gas or liquid into the surface of a solid where they are held by intermolecular forces to the solid molecules is called –

A	Dispersion	B	Distribution
C	Adoption	D	Adsorption

271) What is the movement of the surface of a liquid up or down a narrow tube placed in a liquid, caused by the surface tension of the liquid called?

(A) Centripetal action   (B) Capillary action
(C) Reverse action   (D) Extreme action

272) What is the SI unit of electric charge produced by the flow of one ampere of current in one second?

(A) Farad   (B) Siemen
(C) Coulomb   (D) Hertz

273) What is the capacity of a body or system to do work called?

(A) Power   (B) Strength
(C) Energy   (D) Stamina

274) What is the strong magnetism that can be induced in Iron & certain other metals called?

(A) Electromagnetism   (B) Ferro-magnetism
(C) Chromo-magnetism   (D) Cupro-magnetism

275) Who was the first to detect Radio waves?

(A) Marconi   (B) James Maxwell
(C) Heinrich Hertz   (D) Nicola Tesla

276) Which instrument is used to determine the distance travelled in a vehicle?

(A) Tachometer   (B) Speedometer
(C) Milometer   (D) Sonometer

277) If a lightweight & a heavyweight material are dropped through a vacuum at the same time which will reach down first?

| A | Heavyweight | | B | Lightweight | |
| C | Both at same time | | D | None of these | |

278) Who first treated zero as a number & showed its mathematical operations?

| A | Aryabhata | | B | Bhaskara | |
| C | Ramanujan | | D | Brahmagupta | |

279) What falls continuously down the entire surface of the earth, whether it is day or night?

| A | Cosmic ray | | B | Cosmic dust | |
| C | Both of above | | D | Solar wind | |

280) What is the time required for the radioactivity of a sample of a radioactive isotope to decrease to half its value called?

| A | Half-time | | B | Half-life | |
| C | Half-value | | D | Half-energy | |

LITERATURE

281) What is a story featuring with personifying animals, having moral values called?

| A | Classic | B | Epic |
| C | Fable | D | Fairy Tale |

282) Who wrote the most famous fairy tales - Snow White, Cinderella, Hansel & Gretel etc., in the 19th century?

| A | Jakob Grimm | B | Wilhelm Grimm |
| C | Both of above | D | Hans Anderson |

283) Which was the last letter added to the English alphabet making it to 26 altogether?

| A | J | B | U |
| C | W | D | Y |

284) Which word in English language has the most definitions of about 50 nouns & 125 verbs?

| A | Think | B | There |
| C | Take | D | Set |

285) What word is used in lieu of - 'Many'?

| A | Mega | B | Mono |
| C | Multi | D | Pre |

286) Which six letter word was nominated as the most beautiful word in English?

| A | Beauty | B | Humour |
| C | Mother | D | Lovely |

287) The eighth and the last book of Harry Potter series of books by J.K. Rowling is - Harry Potter & the -

| A | Half Blood Prince | B | Cursed Child |
| C | Deathly Hallows | D | Order of Phoenix |

288) Who is known as the father of English language & English literature?

- (A) E.M. Forrester
- (B) Shakespeare
- (C) Geoffrey Chaucer
- (D) Geoffrey Boycott

289) Which word in the English language has all the letters in alphabetical order?

- (A) Almost
- (B) Abduct
- (C) Acquit
- (D) Adept

290) Writers from which country have won the most number of Nobel Prizes (16) for literature so far?

- (A) UK
- (B) USA
- (C) France
- (D) Germany

291) Who wrote the most number of non-fictions of about 650 among the Indian writers?

- (A) J. Krishnamurthy
- (B) S. Radhakrishnan
- (C) R.K. Narayan
- (D) Osho Rajneesh

292) Which is the most frequently used alphabet in the English language?

- (A) A
- (B) E
- (C) S
- (D) T

293) Who among these was the most popular short-story writer?

- (A) George Eliot
- (B) D.H. Lawrence
- (C) Oliver Henry
- (D) Thomas Hardy

294) Which of these series of children's books were not written by Enid Blyton?

- (A) Noddy
- (B) Nancy Drew
- (C) Famous 5
- (D) Secret 7

295) Who wrote the original version of Ramayana?

A. Varahamihira | B. Valmiki
C. C. Rajagopalachari | D. R.K. Narayan

296) Who wrote the series of seven books - 'The Chronicles of Narnia'?

A. Carl Lewis | B. C.S. Lewis
C. George Lucas | D. Michael Crichton

297) In which of these words, the vowels figure in the ascending order?

A. Cautions | B. Facetious
C. Malicious | D. Ferocious

298) Which among these is not a fairy tale?

A. Cinderella | B. Thumbelina
C. Sleeping Beauty | D. Tom Sawyer

299) What is the Anagram for Mother-in law?

A. Watermelon | B. Woman Hitler
C. Wonderment | D. Waistband

300) Which author of Indian origin is awarded Man - Booker prize in 2006 for 'The Inheritance of Loss'?

A. Anita Desai | B. Kiran Desai
C. Indira Goswami | D. Amrita Pritam

301) Which book of Dan Brown is sold more than 80 million copies world wide & also made into film?

A. Angels & Demons | B. Digital Fortress
C. Da Vinci Code | D. The Lost Symbol

302) Who wrote the series of books 'Lord of the rings' which were also made into films?

A. J.R.R. Tolkien | B. J.K. Rowling
C. George Lucas | D. Michael Crichton

303) Which play among these was not written by William Shakespeare?

| A Hamlet | B The Mouse Trap |
| C Romeo Juliet | D As you like it |

304) Which word among these is without any vowels of the English alphabet?

| A Wryness | B Xylem |
| C Rhythm | D Typhus |

305) Which of these fairy tales was not written by Hans - Christian Andersen?

| A Alice in Wonderland | B Thumbelina |
| C The Little Mermaid | D The Tin Soldier |

306) Which among these classical novels was not written by Bronte sisters, who were three all died in their 30s?

| A Jane Eyre | B Agnes Grey |
| C Wuthering heights | D Silas Marner |

307) Whose poems were translated into more languages than any other British poets, apart from Shakespeare?

| A Lord Byron | B John Keats |
| C Robert Burns | D John Milton |

308) Which among these is the world's most popular poem written by Rudyard Kipling?

| A Just so stories | B If |
| C Kim | D Jungle Book |

309) Which classical work of Robert Louis Stevenson was left incompleted?

| A Treasure Island | B Kidnapped |
| C Weir of Hermiston | D Dr. Jekyll & Mr.Hyde |

310) Which of these books written by Salman Rushdie is a collection of Non-fiction?

(A) The moor's last sigh   (B) Imaginary homelands
(C) In good faith   (D) Step across this line

311) How much was paid as an advance by Bloomsbury publisher to JK Rowling's first book 'Harry Potter & the Philosopher's Stone'?

(A) UK £ 1000   (B) UK £ 10,000
(C) UK £ 100,000   (D) UK £ million

312) Who was the most famous non-fiction writer wrote mostly on self-development titles?

(A) Dale Brown   (B) Dale Carnegie
(C) G.K. Chesterton   (D) John Cheever

313) Who among these was a Russian-born American Bio-chemist & science fiction writer?

(A) Isaac Newton   (B) Isaac Asimov
(C) Leo Tolstoy   (D) Anton Chekov

314) Who wrote the 'Shiva Trilogy' – which become the fastest selling book series in the history of Indian Publishing?

(A) Aravind Adiga   (B) Amitav Ghosh
(C) Ashwin Sanghi   (D) Amish Tripathi

315) Which of these books was not written by Lebanese born US writer Kahlil Gibran?

(A) The Prophet   (B) Good Shepherd
(C) The Madman   (D) Jesus-The Son of Man

316) Who is the world's most prolific children's writer with more than 800 titles?

(A) Brother Grimm
(B) Hans Christian Andersen
(C) Enid Blyton
(D) Roald Dahl

317) Which book is estimated to have 900 million copies in print, only next to the Bible in the world?

(A) Ramayana
(B) Mao's Little Red Book
(C) Bhagvadgita
(D) Guinness book of World Records

318) Who among these was not a Bronte sister?

(A) Emily
(B) Charlotte
(C) Esther
(D) Anne

319) Which Indian author won the Pulitzer Prize for her short story collection titled 'The Interpreter of Maladies'?

(A) Jhumpa Lahiri
(B) Indira Goswami
(C) Kamala Das
(D) Manjula Padmanaban

320) What are the 14 line poems often made up of 8 stanzas & 6 lines?

(A) Prose
(B) Poetry
(C) Sonnets
(D) Lyrics

321) What is the title of former Pakistan president Parvez Musharaf's autobiography?

(A) Wings of Fire
(B) Arms of Fire
(C) In the line of Fire
(D) In the path of Fire

322) Which among these books was not written by Kalidas?

(A) Raghu Vamsa
(B) Shakuntala
(C) Meghdoot
(D) Kadambari

323) Who was the blind poet who dictated to his daughter to write the Epic poems – Paradise Lost & Paradise Regained?

(A) John Miller	(B) John Milton
(C) ST Coleridge	(D) William Blake

324) What is the fictitious name of the town in R.K. Narayan's novels?

(A) Paramakudi	(B) Lalgudi
(C) Malgudi	(D) Karaikudi

325) Who was also known as Shakespeare of India?

(A) Kalidas	(B) Kabirdas
(C) Tulsidas	(D) Mohandas

326) What is the title of collection of poems by Rabindranath Tagore, which got him the Nobel Prize for literature?

(A) Gitanjali	(B) Shradanjali
(C) Kalanjali	(D) Kavyanjali

327) Which among these books was not written by Dominique Lapierre?

(A) Freedom at Midnight	(B) The Last Mughal
(C) Is Paris Burning	(D) O'Jerusalem

328) Who was the first author of Indian origin to win Man Booker Prize?

(A) Salman Rushdie	(B) Rudyard Kipling
(C) Roald Dahl	(D) V.S. Naipaul

329) Which among these was written Earlier?

(A) Puranas	(B) Vedas
(C) Itihasas	(D) Upanishads

330) Which of these books was not written by Pandit Jawaharlal Nehru?

(A)	Glimpses of World History	(B)	Nehru An Autobiography
(C)	Discovery of India	(D)	A Passage to India

331) What is the Japanese poem of 3 lines with an exact number of 17 syllables per line 5-7-5, written by Matsuo Basho?

(A)	Kaiku	(B)	Haiku
(C)	Matsku	(D)	Bashku

332) Who wrote the classical work 'Black Beauty'?

(A)	Mark Twain	(B)	Jane Austen
(C)	Jules Verne	(D)	Anna Sewell

333) Which American university awards the Pulitzer Prize for excellence in literature?

(A)	Harvard	(B)	Stanford
(C)	Columbia	(D)	California

334) Who wrote the best selling book about the nature of Black holes in space – 'A Brief History of Time'?

(A)	Stephen Hawking	(B)	Stephen Coonts
(C)	Alvin Toffler	(D)	Allan Cole

335) Which national leader's auto-biography is titled 'A Long Walk to Freedom'?

(A)	Abraham Lincoln	(B)	George Washington
(C)	Nelson Mandela	(D)	Vladimir Lenin

336) Which word is not a palindrome, that which cannot be read backwards as the same word?

(A)	Malayalam	(B)	Madam 'I' m Adam
(C)	Race car	(D)	Urdu

337) Who wrote the ever best selling stories of Sherlock Holmes detective stories?

(A) Arthur Clarke
(B) Arthur Miller
(C) Sir Arthur Conan Doyle
(D) Arthur Wilson

338) By what pen name Mary Ann Evans wrote the great novels 'Middle March' & 'Mill on the Floss'?

(A) Thomas Hardy
(B) Howard Pyle
(C) George Eliot
(D) Emile Zola

339) Who wrote the great epics Odyssey & Iliad in the 7th century BC?

(A) Miller
(B) Homer
(C) Roger
(D) Gower

340) Which poet's work was 'Book of Non-sense' & who popularized the humorous 5 line poems called 'Limericks'?

(A) Edward Jones
(B) Edward Thomas
(C) Edward Lear
(D) Edward John

341) Which of these play was not written by George Bernard Shaw?

(A) Twelfth Night
(B) Widower's Houses
(C) Saint Joan
(D) Pygmalion

342) Who was paid the highest advance of about US $ 12 million for a non-fiction?

(A) Hillary Clinton
(B) Bill Clinton
(C) Pope John Paul
(D) Collin Powell

343) Who among these is the world's most popular writer on Feng-Shui?

(A) Sun Tzu
(B) Ann Tsu
(C) Lilian Woo
(D) Lilian Too

344) Who was the most famous best selling author, wrote over 720 fictions & sold more than one billion copies in 36 languages worldwide?

(A) Barbara Taylor Bradford   (B) Barbara Cartland
(C) Barbara Delinsky   (D) Barbara Michaels

345) Which among these classical works is not written by Charles Dickens?

(A) Oliver Twist   (B) Man in the Iron Mask
(C) Nicholas Nickleby   (D) Pickwick Papers

346) Which of these books was written by Roald Dahl?

(A) Heidi   (B) Little Women
(C) Matilda   (D) Moby Dick

347) In which street was Sherlock Holmes said to have lived in Conan Doyle's work?

(A) Downing Street   (B) Baker Street
(C) Cook Street   (D) Chef Street

348) Which novel is about the family life of four sisters during American civil war, written by Louisa May Alcott?

(A) Diary of a young girl   (B) Anna Karenina
(C) Portrait of a lady   (D) Little women

349) Which novel among these was not written by Jane Austen?

(A) Pride & Prejudice   (B) Emma
(C) Sons & Lovers   (D) Sense & Sensibility

350) Who was the first English writer to win Nobel Prize for literature, who was born in Mumbai, India?

(A) Bertrand Russell   (B) Rudyard Kipling
(C) John Galsworthy   (D) Roald Dahl

351) Which writer was an Indian born, educated in England, served five years in Burmese police & wrote Animal Farm?

| A | George Orwell | B | Emile Zola |
| C | Howard Pyle | D | Somerset Maugham |

352) Which philosopher - writer wrote the Dialogues, Republic & Phaedo?

| A | Socrates | B | Aristotle |
| C | Plato | D | Voltaire |

353) What is the amount of cash reward along with the Man Booker Prize (UK)?

| A | UK £ 10000 | B | UK £ 25000 |
| C | UK £ 50000 | D | UK £ 100,000 |

354) What is the name of Sherlock Holmes' assistant in Conan Doyle's stories?

| A | Dr.Waterman | B | Dr.Watson |
| C | Dr.No | D | Dr.Jekyll |

355) Which among these books – a children's fiction, is co-written by Stephen Hawking and his daughter Lucy?

| A | George's secret key to the Universe | B | George's cosmic treasure hunt |
| C | Both of above | D | A Brief History of Time |

356) What goes before woman & mermaid in the title of a book?

| A | Good | B | Pretty |
| C | Little | D | Ugly |

357) Who is Bagheera in Rudyard Kipling's – The Jungle Book?

| A | Snake | B | Panther |
| C | Lion | D | Tiger |

358) Who was the first woman to receive the 'Sahitya Akademi award?

(A) Amrita Pritam	(B) Sarojini Naidu
(C) Indira Goswami	(D) Kamala Das

359) Who wrote the best selling book - 'The Argumentative Indian'?

(A) Arun Shourie	(B) Arun Phoori
(C) Arun Jaitley	(D) Amartya Sen

360) Which among these books was not written by the former Indian President Dr. A.P.J. Abdul Kalam?

(A) India-Vision 2020	(B) We Indians
(C) Ignited Minds	(D) Wings of Fire

361) Who wrote the best selling books Fountain Head & Atlas shrugged?

(A) Anne Rice	(B) Ayn Rand
(C) Anne Frank	(D) Anne Smith

362) How many capital letters of English alphabets look the same in both front & rear views?

(A) 6	(B) 9
(C) 11	(D) 14

363) Which language's script is written from right to left?

(A) Arabic	(B) Urdu
(C) Both of above	(D) Hebrew

364) Which language has the least number of alphabet?

(A) Hindi	(B) English
(C) Japanese	(D) Chinese

365) Which is the longest play out of 37 written by William Shakespeare?

(A) Hamlet	(B) Macbeth
(C) Othello	(D) Romeo & Juliet

366) In a Standard English dictionary, which letter has the least number of words?

(A) W
(B) X
(C) Y
(D) Z

367) Who wrote the collection of poems titled 'Pukhraj'?

(A) Salim
(B) Sameer
(C) Gulzar
(D) Javed Akhthar

368) Whose autography was titled as 'My Autobiography'?

(A) Indira Gandhi
(B) Bill Clinton
(C) Pamela Anderson
(D) Charlie Chaplin

369) Which is the 20th century's longest novel with more than 500,000 words?

(A) A Suitable girl
(B) A Suitable boy
(C) Sacred games
(D) War & peace

370) Which among these is the first novel written by R.K. Narayan?

(A) The Guide
(B) Malgudi days
(C) Swami & Friends
(D) Waiting for Mahatma

371) Which is an all time best selling reference book in the world?

(A) Encyclopedia Britannica
(B) Guinness book of World Records
(C) DK's Visual Dictionary
(D) Oxford Concise Dictionary

372) Who wrote the poem volumes - songs of innocence, songs of experience & Milton?

(A) S.T. Coleridge
(B) Robert Williams
(C) William Golding
(D) William Blake

373) Which among these classical novels was not written by Thomas Hardy?

(A) Far from the madding crowd
(B) Crime & Punishment
(C) Jude the obscure
(D) Mayor of caster bridge

374) Who wrote the tale of Peter Rabbit which was rejected by 6 publishers, later published by the authoress herself & sold well?

| (A) Katherine Mayo | (B) Beatrix Potter |
| (C) Gloria Steinem | (D) Romila Thapar |

375) What was the pen name of Samuel Langhorne Clemens, who wrote the Adventures of Tom Sawyer & Huckleberry Finn?

| (A) Hermann Melville | (B) H.G. Wells |
| (C) Mark Twain | (D) Rudyard Kipling |

376) Salman Rushdie was awarded Booker prize for which of these books?

| (A) Midnight's Children | (B) The ground beneath her feet |
| (C) The Satanic Verses | (D) Shalimar the clown |

377) Who is the most frequently cited author of any other?

| (A) Charles Dickens | (B) Conan Doyle |
| (C) William Shakespeare | (D) Oscar Wilde |

378) Which philosopher said, 'The last words are for fools who have not said enough'?

| (A) George Bernard Shaw | (B) Karl Marx |
| (C) Hegel | (D) Machiavelli |

379) Who is the writer from Turkey who wrote 'Istanbul memories & the city' awarded the Nobel Prize for literature in 2006?

| (A) Orhan Pamuk | (B) Harold Pinter |
| (C) Elfriede Jelinek | (D) Imre Kertesz |

380) Who was the greatest of Greek dramatists, wrote about 80 plays?

| (A) Empedocles | (B) Euripides |
| (C) Aeschylus | (D) Plutarch |

381) Which among these books is the debut novel of Indian – Australian writer Aravind Adiga, which won him Man Booker in 2008?

A) The Elephant
B) The White Tiger
C) Between the Assassinations
D) The Last Man in Tower

382) Who is the South African writer having won Booker prize twice & also a Nobel Prize for literature?

A) Albert Lutuli
B) J.M. Coetzee
C) Nadine Gordimer
D) F.W. de Klerk

383) The gentleman's gentleman – Jeeves, is a character of which of these writers?

A) P.G. Wodehouse
B) Roald Dahl
C) G.K. Chesterton
D) Emile Zola

384) Which among these books is sold more than 50 million copies and had been translated into 42 languages?

A) Gone with the wind
B) Lewis's Word power made easy
C) Spock's Baby & Child Care
D) Roget's Thesaurus

385) Who wrote the greatest Tamil Epic – Silappadikaram (The Bejewelled Anklet)?

A) Kamban
B) Bharathiyar
C) Ilango Adigal
D) Seethalai Sathanar

386) Which is the World's largest bookstore chain with over 700 stores and over 600 college bookstores?

A) Borders - USA
B) Barnes & Noble - USA
C) Weltbild - Germany
D) W.H. Smith - UK

387) Which is the most frequently used word in written English?

- A) The
- B) Is
- C) A
- D) To

388) Which among these classic novels is not written by David Herbert Lawrence?

- A) Lady Chatterley's Lover
- B) Rainbow
- C) Sons & Lovers
- D) Beloved

389) Who wrote the most famous terrific horror story – Frankenstein, at the age of just 21 years?

- A) Percy Shelley
- B) Mary Shelley
- C) Bram Stoker
- D) Edgar Allan Poe

390) Who is the most famous writer of Astrological books better known as 'Cheiro'?

- A) William L.Shirer
- B) Luigi Pirandello
- C) Eugeneo O'Neill
- D) Count Louis Hamon

391) Who dared to reject the Sahitya Akademi award for her book 'The Algebra of infinite Justice'?

- A) Anita Desai
- B) Kavya Viswanathan
- C) Arundhathi Roy
- D) Jhumpa Lahiri

392) Which among these is the detective character appears in Agatha Christie's novels?

- A) Hercule Poirot
- B) Miss Marple
- C) Both of above
- D) Perry Mason

393) Who was the co-author of 'Moonstone' & 'The Woman in White', with Charles Dickens?

- A) Wilkie Collins
- B) Eileen Collins
- C) Jackie Collins
- D) Peter Collins

394) Who was the Italian writer who wrote the novels Foucault's Pendulum & A theory of semiotics?

(A) Danti Aligheiri
(B) Umberto Eco
(C) Louis Fischer
(D) J.J. Rousseau

395) Name the two heroes in Shakespeare's 'The two gentlemen of Verona' –

(A) Terence Hill & Poud Spencer
(B) Lawry & Simpson
(C) Valentine & Proteus
(D) Clinton & Bush

396) Which was the first book of Salman Rushdie's, published in 1975?

(A) Satanic Verses
(B) Shalimar the Clown
(C) Grimus
(D) Midnight's Children

397) Which among these Tamil writer is awarded the 'Gnanpith'?

(A) Jayakanthan
(B) Balakumaran
(C) Sujatha
(D) Vairamuthu

398) Who was the Austrian physician & also the popular writer on psycho-analysis?

(A) Edward de Bono
(B) Sigmund Freud
(C) Lucian Freud
(D) Anna Freud

399) Who was the first non-European to win the Nobel Prize for literature in 1913?

(A) Rabindranath Tagore
(B) Sinclair Lewis
(C) William Faulkner
(D) Henry Kissinger

400) Who among these great leaders was awarded Nobel Prize for literature?

(A) Nelson Mandela
(B) Winston Churchill
(C) Mikhail S.Gorbhachev
(D) Woodrow Wilson

Quiz Time: Literature

401) How many books were written by Agatha Christie who wrote 'The Mouse Trap' – the longest-run play (25000 performances until 2012)?

(A) 36	(B) 57
(C) 87	(D) 147

402) Which word uses the most number of vowels consecutively?

(A) Queasy	(B) Quiet
(C) Quaint	(D) Queueing

403) Who was the first to receive Sahitya Akademi award for writing in English?

(A) Raja Rao	(B) R.K. Narayan
(C) Mulk Raj Anand	(D) Nirad C. Chaudhri

404) Which writer's lawyer-detective is Perry Mason?

(A) Erle Stanley Gardner	(B) Ellery Queen
(C) William Darymple	(D) Ralph Ellison

405) Which among these book was not written by Sidney Sheldon?

(A) Day of the Jackal	(B) Best laid Plans
(C) The other side of Midnight	(D) The other side of Me

406) Which book was last & incomplete, written by Charles Dickens?

(A) Our Mutual Friend	(B) Mystery of Edwin Drood
(C) Great Expectations	(D) Little Dorrit

407) Who wrote the series of books 'Animorphs'?

(A) K.A. Applegate	(B) R.L. Stine
(C) Aldous Huxley	(D) Mary Shelley

408) Who was the first author to submit the typewritten manuscript?

(A) Victor Hugo	(B) Leo Tolstoy
(C) Mark Twain	(D) Charles Dickens

409) Which of these novels was not written by Jeffrey Archer?

A	Kane & Abel	B	Prodigal Daughter
C	Cat O'nine tales	D	Future Shock

410) What are the series of fantasy books, written by Eoin Colfer?

A	Goosebumps	B	Artemis Fowl
C	Star Trek	D	Star Wars

411) To commemorate which author's death anniversary, UNESCO celebrates the 'World Book Day'?

A	Conan Doyle	B	Oscar Wilde
C	William Shakespeare	D	Jane Austen

412) Who created the most famous character 'James Bond 007'?

A	Ian Fleming	B	Irwin Fleming
C	Robert Broccoli	D	Albert Broccoli

413) Which of these books was not written by Shoba de?

A	Socialite evenings	B	Speed post
C	The better man	D	Spouse

414) Which author's short story collection is titled 'Mansarovar'?

A	Nirad C. Chaudhri	B	Prem Chand
C	Anita Desai	D	Jhumpa Lahiri

415) Which among these best selling novels was not written by the Brazilian writer – Paulo Coelho?

A	The Alchemist	B	Zahir
C	Eleven minute	D	Catch-22

416) Sketch the period of Shakespeare's–

A	1364-1416	B	1474-1526
C	1564-1616	D	1636-1688

417) What was the amazing number of characters portrayed in Leo Tolstoy's 'War & Peace', which had about 700,000 words?

(A) 198	(B) 286
(C) 539	(D) 789

418) Who was not one of the Three Musketeers in the novel of the same title by Alexander Dumas?

(A) Athos	(B) Porthos
(C) Aramis	(D) Nurmis

419) What is the total number of books in the Bible, Old Testament & New Testament together?

(A) 27	(B) 39
(C) 66	(D) 93

420) For how many Indian languages, the Sahitya Akademi award for literature is extended?

(A) 12	(B) 18
(C) 22	(D) 26

WORLD RELIGIONS

421) Which is the world's oldest religion since 1500 BC?

(A) Judaism   (B) Confucianism
(C) Hinduism   (D) Buddhism

422) Which is the world's youngest religion?

(A) Christianity   (B) Islam
(C) Taoism   (D) Buddhism

423) Who was the father of Judaism, receives 'Ten Commandments' from the God which is the law basis for the Jews?

(A) Abraham   (B) Isaac
(C) Jacob   (D) Moses

424) Who was the founder of Sikh religion – Sikhism?

(A) Guru Nanak   (B) Gobind Singh
(C) Harkishan Singh   (D) Harbhajan Singh

425) Which is the holiest city of Hinduism, on the banks of the river Ganges in India?

(A) Benares   (B) Varanasi
(C) Kasi   (D) All of these

426) Which scriptures of Hinduism means the 'Song of the Lord'?

(A) Puranas   (B) Vedas
(C) Bhagavadgita   (D) Ramayana

427) When was Buddhism founded by Buddha (Siddharth), who was a born prince in India?

(A) 10th century BC   (B) 6th Century BC
(C) 6th Century AD   (D) 10th Century AD

428) Who were the parents of prophet Mohamed?

Ⓐ Abdullah - Amina	Ⓑ Abdullah - Fatima
Ⓒ Amanullah - Amina	Ⓓ Amanullah - Fatima

429) Who were the parents of Jesus Christ?

Ⓐ Esther - Williams	Ⓑ Mary - Joseph
Ⓒ Emily - Jacob	Ⓓ Mary - Jacob

430) What is the Hindu's religious song (or) hymn in praise of God, sung in groups accompanied by musical instruments called?

Ⓐ Keerthanas	Ⓑ Bhajans
Ⓒ Ghazals	Ⓓ Shlokas

431) In Hinduism, what is the name given to a person of divine or most holy or true reality?

Ⓐ Raman	Ⓑ Kaman
Ⓒ Brahman	Ⓓ Aryan

432) What is the sacred name of God, used by the Jewish people?

Ⓐ Jacob	Ⓑ Joseph
Ⓒ Jehovah	Ⓓ Messiah

433) Which Hindu God is regarded as the God of good beginnings, a symbol of luck & wealth in business and daily life?

Ⓐ Ganesha	Ⓑ Shiva
Ⓒ Vishnu	Ⓓ All of these

434) The Islamic calendar 'Hijri' starts from –

Ⓐ 570 AD	Ⓑ 622 AD
Ⓒ 632 AD	Ⓓ 786 AD

435) What is the most common first name of a person around the world?

(A) Chang	(B) Mohamed
(C) Lee	(D) Smith

436) Where was Buddhism first preached?

(A) India	(B) Tibet
(C) Bhutan	(D) Thailand

437) What is the name of boat, which is described in the Jewish scriptures was built by Noah & his family?

(A) Gondola	(B) Catamaran
(C) Ark	(D) Yacht

438) In which Hindu's festival, the goddess of good fortune - Lakshmi, visits home which are lit with lamps bringing with her good fortune for the coming year?

(A) Sankranti	(B) Holi
(C) Dussehra	(D) Diwali

439) What festival is celebrated by Muslims at the end of Ramadan in which poor are given alms & the children are presented with gifts?

(A) Ramzan	(B) Bakrid
(C) Milad-un-nabi	(D) Muharram

440) Who is the Hero of Hindu's epic 'Ramayana'?

(A) Rama	(B) Ravana
(C) Lakshmana	(D) Hanuman

441) What is the day of Jesus Christ's crucifixion called as?

(A) Good Friday	(B) Bad Friday
(C) Friday the 13th	(D) All of these

442) Which among these is not one of the five Ks of Sikhism?

A) Kesh & Kangha   B) Kara & Kaccha
C) Kirpan   D) Kaftan

443) What is the place of worship for Jews called?

A) Chapel   B) Monaestery
C) Synagogue   D) Monogogue

444) What were the Hindu scriptures written between 800 & 400 BC in which the understanding of Brahman explained?

A) Puranas   B) Itihas
C) Upanishads   D) Perishads

445) How Islam is followed by the Muslims worldwide as they were told to?

A) As a religion   B) As the way of life
C) As a custom   D) All of these

446) Which among these religion is not a monotheistic – believing in one God?

A) Christianity   B) Judaism
C) Hinduism   D) Islam

447) Who was prophet Mohamed's uncle who took charge of him at the age of 8, after his grandfather's death?

A) Abu-Muttalib   B) Abu-Talib
C) Abu-Lahab   D) Abbas

448) Which is the youngest religion in India, founded about 500 years ago – a fusion of Hinduism & Islam?

A) Jainism   B) Mahavirs
C) Sikhism   D) Parsis

449) Who was the disciple & also a close friend of Jesus Christ, originally named Simon?

A	St.Paul	B	St.Peter
C	St.Joseph	D	St.George

450) What is the holy scriptures of Jewish people?

A	Borah	B	Dorah
C	Morah	D	Torah

451) Which religion believes in reincarnation – the idea describes the cycles of rebirth?

A	Sikhism	B	Hinduism
C	Islam	D	Christianity

452) How the Greek Goddess of victory is known as?

A	Nemesis	B	Nike
C	Poseidon	D	Athena

453) What the verse in Quran – "Fight against those who fight against you, but do not trespass (by attacking first)" refers to?

A	Holy war	B	Sacred war
C	Martyrdom	D	All of these

454) Which religious people worship fire as God?

A	Sikhs & Jews	B	Jains & Christians
C	Buddhists & Parsis	D	Parsis & Hindus

455) Which among these is a top pilgrimage destination for Indians?

A	Varanasi - UP	B	Puri - Orissa
C	Vaishno Devi - J&K	D	Tirupati - AP

456) Who was the first person to win the 'Templeton Prize' referred to as the Nobel Prize for religion?

(A) Mother Teresa	(B) Swami Vivekananda
(C) Dalai Lama	(D) Sai Baba

457) What is the name of town in Palestine where Jesus Christ was born?

(A) Nazareth	(B) Bethlehem
(C) Tiberias	(D) Hebron

458) What is the numerical value of the Islamic verse in Arabic, which means 'In the name of Allah, the most beneficent & the Merciful'?

(A) 456	(B) 567
(C) 786	(D) 987

459) Where do Sikhs worship & meet?

(A) Gyan Mandir	(B) Seva Sadan
(C) Gurudwara	(D) Bhilwara

460) When was prophet Mohamed born at Mecca in Saudi Arabia?

(A) 420 BC	(B) 240 BC
(C) 420 AD	(D) 570 AD

461) Which is one of the oldest main scriptures of Hinduism made up of more than 1000 hymns, also known as songs of knowledge'?

(A) Rig-veda	(B) Yajur-veda
(C) Sama-veda	(D) Atharva-veda

462) How many books were there in the Hebrew Scriptures called the 'Old Testament'?

(A) 18	(B) 27
(C) 30	(D) 39

463) What is the name given to a large Church were the bishop has his throne?

A) Chapel
B) Cathedral
C) Monastery
D) Asylum

464) What is the holy scriptures of Sikh religion known as?

A) Guru Nanak Sahib
B) Guru Granth Sahib
C) Har Gobind Sahib
D) Har Granth Sahib

465) In Hindu mythology, which God is known as the preserver?

A) Brahma
B) Vishnu
C) Shiva
D) Indra

466) Of the four noble truths of Buddhism, which one is original to Buddha & the rest based on Hinduism?

A) Fact of suffering
B) Cause of suffering
C) End of suffering
D) Escape from suffering

467) What was prophet Mohamed's age when he married Khadija – a widowed merchant aged 40?

A) 25
B) 28
C) 32
D) 38

468) What is the name for a community of nuns-women, who made holy vows & live together?

A) Convent
B) Covenant
C) Communent
D) Immanent

469) In Hindu caste system, who were merchants, professionals & agriculturalists?

A) Brahmans
B) Shudras
C) Kshatriyas
D) Vaisyas

470) How the Roman Goddess of wisdom is known as?

A	Venus	B	Victoria
C	Minerva	D	Flora

471) Who was the favourite & the only virgin girl prophet Mohamed married, while others were widows?

A	Umm Salma	B	Hafsa
C	Aisha	D	Umm Habiba

472) At where the Christians are being baptised by totally immersed in water rather than having holy water sprinkled on them?

A	Catholic Church	B	Baptist Church
C	Pentecostal Church	D	Methodist Church

473) How the Hindu Goddess of power & destruction known as?

A	Kali	B	Parvati
C	Durga	D	Indrani

474) Who among these are considered as non-Muslims?

A	Sunni's	B	Shii'tes
C	Wahabi's	D	Bahai's

475) Who believes that their religion was evolved by 24 Tirthankaras – the perfect beings?

A	Buddhists	B	Sikhs
C	Jains	D	Hindus

476) Which Christian sect has the most members of over one billion?

A	Orthodox	B	Roman Catholic
C	Pentecostal	D	Lutheran

477) At what age, Parsi's initiation ceremony called 'Navjote' is performed?

| (A) 5 years | (B) 7 years |
| (C) 12 years | (D) 18 years |

478) Which is the ancient Persian religion based upon the dual principles of Ormuzd, the God of light & good and also Ahriman, the God of darkness & Evil?

| (A) Skimbanguism | (B) Zoroastrianism |
| (C) Amish | (D) Epis Copal |

479) What is the term for Islamic way of cutting the prescribed poultry or cattle's half neck for meat?

| (A) Bilal | (B) Halal |
| (C) Kalal | (D) Jalal |

480) Who was the mother of Lord Mahavira?

| (A) Trisha | (B) Vaishnavi |
| (C) Trishala | (D) Kundavi |

481) To which God the Gayatri Mantra is addressed by the Hindus?

| (A) Indra | (B) Vishnu |
| (C) Surya | (D) Shiva |

482) What are the first four books of New Testament out of 27 that tell the life of Jesus Christ?

| (A) Gospels | (B) Goodnews |
| (C) Both of above | (D) Psalms |

483) To which sect of Muslims, the spiritual leader is Aga Khan?

| (A) Shii'te's | (B) Sunni's |
| (C) Ismaili's | (D) Wahabi's |

484) Who is the Hindu God of disease & healing?

A	Varuna	B	Rudra
C	Agni	D	Dhara

485) Which is the largest theocratic country governed by a religious leader?

A	Vatican	B	Palestine
C	Iran	D	Israel

486) Where in India the only temple dedicated to the Hindu God Brahma - the creator, is situated?

A	Konark	B	Badrinath
C	Pushkar	D	Kedarnath

487) Which country has the highest proportion of 95% Buddhist population?

A	Bhutan	B	Myanmar
C	Cambodia	D	Thailand

488) Which among these is a collection of Buddha's stories?

A	Hitopadesha	B	Jataka Tales
C	Panchatantra	D	Aesop's Fables

489) How Hazrat Imam Hussain and Hasan were related to prophet Mohamed?

A	Sons	B	Grand sons
C	Uncles	D	Cousins

490) At what age the Roman Catholics are confirmed the Christian rite in which they become adult members?

A	7 years	B	10 years
C	12 years	D	15 years

491) Which Hindu's springtime festival marks the new planting season called as?

| A | Dussehra | B | Vijaya dasami |
| C | Holi | D | Sankranti |

492) Which is the world's largest religious structure covering 402 acres, built for the Hindu God Vishnu?

| A | Batu Caves-Malaysia | B | Angkorwat-Cambodia |
| C | Brahadeeswara Temple-India | D | Sri Rangam Temple-India |

493) In Hindu caste systems, how the untouchables are called as?

| A | Mahajans | B | Girijans |
| C | Harijans | D | Gurujans |

494) Which is the major religion of the world today with over 2 billion followers?

| A | Christianity | B | Islam |
| C | Hinduism | D | Buddhism |

495) Who was Hanuman's father in Hindu mythology?

| A | Vaali | B | Vaayu |
| C | Sugreeva | D | Jambhavaan |

496) To which religion, the two broad divisions called Shwetambar & Digambar are associated with?

| A | Sikhs | B | Jains |
| C | Parsis | D | Buddhists |

497) Which Hindu God is also known as Gopala or Govinda?

| A | Ganesha | B | Indira |
| C | Vishnu | D | Shiva |

498) Which is the fifth pillar (duty) of a Muslim to carry out atleast once in his lifetime in response to Allah?

(A) Kalima (Recitation) (B) Daily Prayers (Namaz)
(C) Alms giving (Zakat) & Fasting (Roza) (D) Pilgrimage to Mecca (Hajj)

499) Who is the leader of the Roman Catholic Christian Church throughout the world?

(A) Pope (B) Bishop
(C) Saint (D) Cardinal

500) Who is regarded as the tenth incarnation (avatar) & also the last of Vishnu in Hinduism?

(A) Rama (B) Krishna
(C) Kalki (D) Balarama

501) Which community in India abandon the dead bodies on mountains for birds to feed with?

(A) Sindhis (B) Parsis
(C) Jains (D) Sikhs

502) Which minority religion ranks three in the Indian population?

(A) Sikhs (B) Christians
(C) Jains (D) Parsis

503) Who was the successor (Caliph) of prophet Mohamed in 632 AD?

(A) Abu Bakr (B) Othman
(C) Omar (D) Ali

504) Whom do Shiite Muslims believe as the successor of prophet Muhammed, but he was the last Caliph (4th)?

(A) Omar (B) Abu Bakr
(C) Othman (D) Ali

505) Which is the first book of Jew's Bible – Old Testament?

A) Genesis
B) Exodus
C) Judges
D) Wisdom

506) Which is the world's first granite temple in India?

A) Brahadeeswar Temple-Tanjore, TN
B) Birla Mandir-Hyderabad
C) Jagannath Temple-Puri
D) Sun Temple-Konark

507) In Ramayana, who was the mother of Rama?

A) Sumitra
B) Kaikeyi
C) Kaushalya
D) Draupadi

508) Who wrote the Hindu's great epic Ramayana?

A) Ved Vyasa
B) Valmiki
C) Vishnu Sharma
D) Kautilya

509) Which is not the name of Hindu's God - Murugan, Ganesha's younger brother?

A) Saravanan
B) Thandapani
C) Kartikeyan
D) Gajapathy

510) Where in India the only mythological theme park is planned to be built?

A) Varanasi
B) Tirupati
C) Amarnath
D) Vaishno Devi

511) At what age, Jesus Christ was crucified?

A) 28 years
B) 33 years
C) 38 years
D) 43 years

512) Which religion is originated from the Japanese folk religion?

A) Taoism
B) Fascism
C) Shintoism
D) Confucianism

513) Who were the sons of Adam, the first man created by God, as told in Bible?

A	Kane & Nobel	B	Cain & Abel
C	Vain & Nobel	D	Peine & Abel

514) Who is regarded as the last & the greatest prophet of Allah - the only God of Islam?

A	Ibrahim	B	Moosa
C	Isa	D	Mohamed

515) What was the original name of prophet Mohamed?

A	Abul Hassan	B	Ubu'l Kassim
C	Abul Obaid	D	Ubu'l Salim

516) In Hindu mythology, who is the younger brother of Indra, also called Upendra?

A	Brahma	B	Vishnu
C	Shiva	D	Ganesha

517) Which country has the largest population of Muslims in the world?

A	Pakistan	B	India
C	Indonesia	D	Bangladesh

518) Which country has the largest population of about 6 million Jewish people in the world?

A	Israel	B	USA
C	France	D	Canada

519) By what name most of popes were referred to?

A	John	B	Gregory
C	Benedict	D	Innocent

520) In Hindu mythology, who is referred to as Goddess of war?

| A | Kali | B | Durga |
| C | Dipti | D | Indrani |

521) Which is the shortest book in the Old Testament?

| A | Daniel | B | Baruch |
| C | Obadiah | D | Nehemiah |

522. What is the name for places of worship of Muslims?

| A | Madarasa | B | Masjid |
| C | Dargah | D | Idgah |

523) Which Hindu God is also known as king of Gods?

| A | Kubera | B | Brahma |
| C | Indra | D | Vishnu |

524) What was the site of Jesus' crucifixion – a common place for execution of criminals in the Roman Empire?

| A | Bethlehem | B | Jerusalem |
| C | Nazareth | D | Golgotha |

525) What is the Islamic festival, which celebrates the obedience of Ibrahim in being prepared to sacrifice his son Ismail to God & also the end of pilgrimage to Mecca (Hajj)?

| A | Bakrid | B | Id-ul-Adha |
| C | Both of above | D | Muharram |

526) Who are appointed by the Pope, most of them reside in Rome & they advise Pope?

| A | Chancellors | B | Cardinals |
| C | Monsignors | D | Abbots |

527) In Hindu mythology, who is regarded as the Sun God?

A Surya
B Vivasan
C Dhatar
D All of these

528) Which is the most visited Hindu temple in India?

A Vaishno Devi-J&K
B Tirumala-Tirupati
C Meenakshi Temple-Madurai
D Vishwanath Temple-Varanasi

529) Which is very occasionally said to be the sixth pillar (duty) in Islam?

A The pilgrimage (Hajj)
B Alms giving (Zakat)
C Formal worship (Namaz)
D Holy war (Jihad)

530) Which is the largest religion without rites such as ceremonies, sacrament & clergy, practiced by over 6 million people in more than 70 countries?

A Shintoism
B Confucianism
C Bahaiism
D Taiosm

531) In Hindu mythology, who is referred to as Goddess of success?

A Kaumudi
B Siddhi
C Candika
D Ardra

532) Which country has the largest Christian's population in the world?

A USA
B Brazil
C Mexico
D China

533) When did prophet Mohamed die at Medina (formerly Yathreb)?

A 8th June 622 AD
B 8th June 632 AD
C 8th January 636 AD
D 8th January 646 AD

534) What is the name of a seven branched candlestick used in Judaism during the seven day festival called 'Hanukkah'?

(A) Menara	(B) Menorah
(C) Kinara	(D) Kenorah

535) In which country, the largest Buddhist temple was built in 8th century at 32m high?

(A) Nepal	(B) Indonesia
(C) Thailand	(D) Japan

536) Taoism is based on whose preaching, which influenced most Chinese people?

(A) Chuang Tzu	(B) Lao-Tse
(C) Mae Se Tung	(D) Sun Tzu

537) Rajneesh Chandra Mohan (alias) Bhagwan Shree Rajneesh (Osho) was born as a –

(A) Christian	(B) Sikh
(C) Jain	(D) Parsi

538) Who is the founder of Bahaiism & proclaimed himself as Bahau'llah in 1863?

(A) Mirza Ali Mohamed	(B) Mirza Hussain Ali
(C) Abdul Baha	(D) Shoghi Effendi

539) Which city was the base for prophet Mohamed before he recaptured Mecca, is also the site of Mohamed's tomb?

(A) Mt. Hira	(B) Mina
(C) Medina	(D) Al-safa

Quiz Time: World Religions

540) What is the Christian festival, which celebrates the resurrection of Jesus known as?

A All souls day
B Easter
C Thanksgiving day
D Boxing day

541) In Hindu mythology, who was the son of Dushyant & Shakuntala?

A Arjuna
B Nakul
C Guha
D Bharata

542) Which country has the highest proportion of 90% Hindus to its population?

A India
B Nepal
C Mauritius
D Guyana

543) Where the largest Synagogue of Jews with a seating capacity of 5500 people is located?

A Tel Aviv-Israel
B Toronto-Canada
C New York-USA
D Paris-France

544) Who were the parents of Gautama Buddha?

A Duryodana-Yashoda
B Suddhodana-Maya
C Siddhartha-Thara
D Aditya-Sara

545) What is the name of Japanese school of Mahayana Buddhism, which emphasizes the value of meditation & intuition?

A Sen
B Den
C Zen
D Zing

546) Which is the world's largest Mosque at 47 acres with total capacity of 300,000 people to pray at a time?

A Blue Mosque-Turkey
B Jum'a Masjid-India
C Shah Faizal Mosque-Pakistan
D Jame'Asr Hassanil Bolkiah Mosque-Brunei

547) Where is the largest Cathedral in the world with a floor area of 121,000 sq.ft?

A St.Peter's Basilica-Vatican
B St.Basil's Church-Moscow
C Westminster Abbey-London
D St.John-The divine-New York

548) Which among these is the largest surviving Zoroastrian community in the world?

A Parsis
B Sindhis
C Kurds
D Bahais

549) Which among these is the exact content of Holy Koran?

A 78000 words
B 114 chapters
C 30 parts
D All of these

550) Where in India the 'Rath Yatra', a big festival is celebrated?

A Somnath temple-Gujarat
B Jagannatha temple-Puri
C Sun temple-Konark
D Brahma temple-Pushkar

551) What is the original name of ISKCON founder A.C. Bhakti Vedanta Swami Prabupada?

A Abhay Deol de
B Abhay Charan de
C Vinay Deol de
D Vinay Charan de

552) What is the name of Bible of 'Taoism' – a 5000 word volume written by Lao-Tse born in 6th century BC?

A Tao Leh Chang
B Tao Teh Ching
C Mao Leh Chang
D Mao Leh Ching

553) Which is the major religion in Japan practiced by more than 50% of the people?

A Buddhism
B Shintoism
C Taoism
D Maoism

554) What is the philosophical denial of the existence of God or any super-natural or super being called?

A	Mysticism	B	Fascism
C	Atheism	D	Agnosticism

555) People of which country practice Confucianism mostly, founded by Confucius in 6th century BC?

A	China	B	Vietnam
C	Cambodia	D	Laos

556) When is the New Year's Day of Bahai's celebrated?

A	January 1st	B	January 14th
C	March 1st	D	March 21st

557) How many names of Allah – the only God of Islam are known of?

A	67	B	78
C	89	D	99

558) What are the Methodist's churches often called as?

A	Cathedral	B	Chapels
C	Minster	D	Monaestry

559) In which Indian city, the biggest religious crowd of 80 million Hindu pilgrims gathered, at a 'half' Kumbh Mela in 2013?

A	Ahmedabad	B	Ghaziabad
C	Allahabad	D	Adilabad

560) Which among these is not one of the 'Panchamahabhoota', according to Hinduism?

A	Earth	B	Fire & Water
C	Universe	D	Air & Sky

✦ ✦ ✦

ANSWERS
CHEMISTRY

1. (B)   Organic Chemistry
2. (B)   0°C
3. (D)   Nucleic
4. (C)   Both of above
5. (D)   Water
6. (C)   Bakelite
7. (A)   Atom
8. (A)   Proton
9. (B)   Kevlar
10. (C)   92
11. (B)   Carbon
12. (D)   All of these
13. (C)   Solid
14. (B)   Evaporation
15. (C)   Transition metals
16. (C)   Salt
17. (A)   Volatile
18. (A)   Uranium
19. (B)   Polymers
20. (C)   88:10:2
21. (A)   Solid carbon dioxide (CO_2)
22. (B)   Half-life
23. (B)   Carbolic acid
24. (C)   Potential of hydrogen
25. (D)   Corrosive reaction
26. (D)   Tungsten
27. (C)   Calcination
28. (A)   Fluoride
29. (A)   Ore
30. (B)   Transuranic elements
31. (B)   Helium
32. (C)   Ammonia
33. (C)   Astatine
34. (A)   Cocaine
35. (B)   Water
36. (D)   Tetraethyl Lead
37. (C)   Borosilicate glass
38. (C)   4
39. (B)   Sodium benzoate

40. (C) Mercury
41. (D) CFCs
42. (C) Asbestos
43. (C) Alloy
44. (C) Chlorofluorocarbon
45. (D) Iridium
46. (B) Crude oil
47. (A) Hydrogen
48. (D) Mango
49. (C) Water
50. (D) Sand (Silica)
51. (D) Sulphur
52. (B) Acid
53. (A) Less than 7.0
54. (A) Iron
55. (D) Remain the same
56. (A) Molecule
57. (B) Aerosols
58. (D) Mica
59. (C) Both of above
60. (D) All of these
61. (A) Diamond
62. (B) Sublimation
63. (B) Chemotherapy
64. (B) More than 100°C
65. (D) Magnesium hydroxide
66. (B) Amalgam
67. (D) Carbohydrates
68. (A) Catalyst
69. (A) Red phosphorus
70. (A) Osmium
71. (C) Hydrochloric acid
72. (A) Ethanal
73. (C) Gyrometallurgy
74. (B) Carbon & Sulphur
75. (B) Humidity
76. (B) Alnico
77. (C) Vanadium
78. (B) Polonium
79. (C) Quark

80. (C) Mass number
81. (B) U^{235}
82. (B) Carbon dioxide
83. (C) Esters
84. (B) Hormones
85. (B) Cotton
86. (D) Lipids
87. (C) Metalloid
88. (A) Codeine
89. (A) Paint
90. (D) All of these
91. (B) Ethanol
92. (D) Ascorbic acid
93. (A) Allotropic form
94. (C) Carbohydrates
95. (B) Sodium pentothal
96. (B) Evaporation
97. (B) Desalination
98. (D) All of these
99. (B) Aliphatic
100. (A) Alkaloid
101. (D) Hydrogen
102. (A) White phosphorus
103. (C) Cinnabar
104. (B) Lithium
105. (A) Thebaine
106. (B) Spirits of salts
107. (D) Bromine
108. (C) Lignocaine
109. (C) Cobalt-60
110. (B) Hydrogen
111. (B) Butane & propane
112. (B) Curium
113. (D) Liquid crystal
114. (B) Methyl isocyanate
115. (D) 75:15:10
116. (B) Lithium (Li)
117. (A) Pepsin
118. (C) Polonium
119. (A) Lanthanides

120. (B) Semtex
121. (C) Diesel
122. (C) HNO_3 & Hcl
123. (B) Chlorine
124. (B) Sodium chloride
125. (C) Gypsum
126. (B) Copper
127. (B) Mordant
128. (C) Rhenium
129. (C) Magnesium
130. (B) Chloroform
131. (A) 1.0
132. (D) All of these
133. (C) Lithium cells
134. (A) Teflon
135. (C) Ester
136. (B) Salicylic acid
137. (D) All of above
138. (A) N-P-K
139. (C) Water
140. (C) Duralumin

PHYSICS

141. (C) Kinetics
142. (B) Electronics
143. (D) Steam Engine
144. (B) Gamma Rays
145. (A) Dynamics
146. (B) Potential energy
147. (B) Meniscus
148. (A) Thermo dynamics
149. (C) Mach number
150. (B) Decibels
151. (D) Oil (or) Grease
152. (A) Anode
153. (A) Ammeter
154. (C) Orange
155. (B) Inferno
156. (A) 340 m/sec
157. (D) Fossil fuels
158. (B) Speed

159. (C) Metals
160. (A) -40°
161. (B) 300,000 km/sec
162. (C) Solid
163. (B) Capillary action
164. (B) Clutch
165. (A) Laser
166. (B) Negatively charged
167. (B) Weight
168. (D) White
169. (A) Kilowatt (kw)
170. (C) Steam Turbines
171. (B) Temperature
172. (B) Velocity
173. (D) All of these
174. (C) Tribology
175. (A) Reynolds number
176. (A) Optics
177. (B) Heat
178. (D) Air
179. (A) Alpha particle
180. (C) Both of above
181. (B) Cybernetics
182. (C) Cubic Capacity
183. (D) Electric energy
184. (B) Volume
185. (D) Oil (fuels)
186. (C) By cooling
187. (C) 4-stroke cycle
188. (D) All of these
189. (C) Radar
190. (A) Gas
191. (D) Distance
192. (B) Sphygmomanometer
193. (D) One-sixth
194. (A) Fuses
195. (D) Thermostat
196. (C) Acceleration
197. (C) Catadioptric telescope
198. (B) Spectrometer
199. (C) Pressure

200. (D) Unit
201. (C) Error
202. (B) Generator
203. (B) Gravitation
204. (C) Holography
205. (C) Supersonic
206. (C) Geothermal energy
207. (A) Fluorescent lamp
208. (C) Electric energy
209. (B) Centrifugal force
210. (B) Picture element
211. (D) All of these
212. (B) Kelvin
213. (B) Convex
214. (B) Cryogenics
215. (A) Density
216. (D) 1.85 km
217. (C) Ampere
218. (C) Elasticity
219. (D) Kilogram
220. (B) Torque
221. (B) Mechanics
222. (B) Power
223. (C) Frequency
224. (B) Geiger-Muller Counter
225. (B) Node
226. (D) Inertia
227. (B) Joule
228. (C) Volume
229. (B) Adiabatic
230. (C) Watt
231. (B) Wavelength
232. (B) Vector quantity
233. (B) Viscosity
234. (B) Ultrasound
235. (B) Thrust
236. (B) Radiation
237. (B) Critical temperature
238. (B) Triboluminescence
239. (C) Lubricants
240. (A) Mass

241. (C) Clinometer
242. (C) Ergonomics
243. (C) Watt
244. (C) Aerodynamics
245. (C) 4.2
246. (B) Magnitude
247. (D) Phase alternation by line
248. (B) Positron
249. (B) Infra-red rays
250. (A) Specific heat capacity
251. (D) Candela
252. (A) Acoustics
253. (B) Sequential & Memory
254. (B) Centre of gravity
255. (B) Rectifier
256. (B) Sound
257. (C) Strain
258. (B) Transformer
259. (B) Pyrometer
260. (C) Plasma
261. (A) Barometer
262. (C) Galvanometer
263. (C) Insulator
264. (B) Load
265. (B) Capacitance
266. (B) Transistor
267. (B) Aberration
268. (B) Adhesion
269. (A) Baryons
270. (D) Adsorption
271. (B) Capillary action
272. (C) Coulomb
273. (C) Energy
274. (B) Ferro-magnetism
275. (C) Heinrich Hertz
276. (B) Speedometer
277. (C) Both at same time
278. (D) Brahmagupta
279. (C) Both of above
280. (B) Half-life

LITERATURE

281. (C) Fable
282. (C) Both of above
283. (B) U
284. (D) Set
285. (C) Multi
286. (C) Mother
287. (B) Cursed Child
288. (C) Geoffrey Chaucer
289. (A) Almost
290. (C) France
291. (D) Osho Rajneesh
292. (B) E
293. (C) Oliver Henry
294. (B) Nancy Drew
295. (B) Valmiki
296. (B) C.S. Lewis
297. (B) Facetious
298. (D) Tom Sawyer
299. (B) Woman Hitler
300. (B) Kiran Desai
301. (C) Da Vinci Code
302. (A) J.R.R. Tolkien
303. (B) Mousetrap
304. (C) Rhythm
305. (A) Alice in Wonderland
306. (D) Silas Marner
307. (C) Robert Burns
308. (B) If
309. (C) Weir of Hermiston
310. (D) Step across this line
311. (B) UK £ 10,000
312. (B) Dale Carnegie
313. (B) Isaac Asimov
314. (D) Amish Tripathi
315. (B) Good Shepherd
316. (C) Enid Blyton
317. (B) Mao's Little Red Book
318. (C) Esther
319. (A) Jhumpa Lahiri

320. (C) Sonnets
321. (C) In the line of Fire
322. (D) Kadambari
323. (B) John Milton
324. (C) Malgudi
325. (A) Kalidas
326. (A) Gitanjali
327. (B) The Last Mughal
328. (D) V.S. Naipaul
329. (B) Vedas
330. (D) A passage to India
331. (B) Haiku
332. (D) Anna Sewell
333. (C) Columbia
334. (A) Stephen Hawking
335. (C) Nelson Mandela
336. (D) Urdu
337. (C) Sir Arthur Conan Doyle
338. (C) George Eliot
339. (B) Homer
340. (C) Edward Lear
341. (A) Twelfth Night
342. (B) Bill Clinton
343. (D) Lilian Too
344. (B) Barbara Cartland
345. (B) Man in the Iron Mask
346. (C) Matilda
347. (B) Baker Street
348. (D) Little women
349. (C) Sons & Lovers
350. (B) Rudyard Kipling
351. (A) George Orwell
352. (C) Plato
353. (C) UK £ 50000
354. (B) Dr.Watson
355. (C) Both of above
356. (C) Little
357. (B) Panther
358. (A) Amrita Pritam
359. (D) Amartya Sen
360. (B) We Indians

Answers

361. (B) Ayn Rand
362. (C) 11
363. (C) Both of above
364. (B) English
365. (A) Hamlet
366. (B) X
367. (C) Gulzar
368. (D) Charlie Chaplin
369. (B) A Suitable boy
370. (C) Swami & Friends
371. (B) Guinness book of World Records
372. (D) William Blake
373. (B) Crime & Punishment
374. (B) Beatrix Potter
375. (C) Mark Twain
376. (A) Midnight's Children
377. (C) William Shakespeare
378. (B) Karl Marx
379. (A) Orhan Pamuk
380. (B) Euripides
381. (B) The White Tiger
382. (B) J.M. Coetzee
383. (A) P.G. Wodehouse
384. (C) Spock's Baby & Child Care
385. (C) Ilango Adigal
386. (B) Barnes & Noble - USA
387. (A) The
388. (D) Beloved
389. (B) Mary Shelley
390. (D) Count Louis Hamon
391. (C) Arundathi Roy
392. (C) Both of above
393. (A) Wilkie Collins
394. (B) Umberto Eco
395. (C) Valentine & Proteus
396. (C) Grimus
397. (A) Jayakanthan
398. (B) Sigmund Freud
399. (A) Rabindranath Tagore
400. (B) Winston Churchill
401. (C) 87

402. (D) Queueing
403. (B) R.K. Narayan
404. (A) Erle Stanley Gardner
405. (A) Day of the Jackal
406. (B) Mystery of Edwin Drood
407. (A) K.A. Applegate
408. (C) Mark Twain
409. (D) Future Shock
410. (B) Artemis Fowl
411. (C) William Shakespeare
412. (A) Ian Fleming
413. (C) The better man
414. (B) Prem Chand
415. (D) Catch-22
416. (C) 1564-1616
417. (C) 539
418. (D) Nurmis
419. (C) 66
420. (C) 22

WORLD RELIGIONS

421. (C) Hinduism
422. (B) Islam
423. (D) Moses
424. (A) Guru Nanak
425. (D) All of these
426. (C) Bhagavadgita
427. (B) 6th Century BC
428. (A) Abdullah - Amina
429. (B) Mary - Joseph
430. (B) Bhajans
431. (C) Brahman
432. (C) Jehovah
433. (A) Ganesha
434. (B) 622 AD
435. (B) Mohamed
436. (A) India
437. (C) Ark
438. (D) Diwali
439. (C) Both of above
440. (A) Rama

441. (A) Good Friday
442. (D) Kaftan
443. (C) Synagogue
444. (C) Upanishads
445. (B) As the way of life
446. (C) Hinduism
447. (B) Abu-Talib
448. (C) Sikhism
449. (B) St.Peter
450. (D) Torah
451. (B) Hinduism
452. (B) Nike
453. (A) Holy war
454. (D) Parsis & Hindus
455. (C) Vaishno Devi - J&K
456. (A) Mother Teresa
457. (B) Bethlehem
458. (C) 786
459. (C) Gurudwara
460. (D) 570 AD
461. (A) Rig-veda
462. (D) 39
463. (B) Cathedral
464. (B) Guru Granth Sahib
465. (B) Vishnu
466. (D) Escape from suffering
467. (A) 25
468. (A) Convent
469. (D) Vaisyas
470. (C) Minerva
471. (C) Aisha
472. (B) Baptist Church
473. (A) Kali
474. (D) Bahai's
475. (C) Jains
476. (B) Roman Catholic
477. (B) 7 years
478. (B) Zoroastrianism
479. (B) Halal
480. (C) Trishala

481. (C) Surya
482. (C) Both of above
483. (C) Ismaili's
484. (B) Rudra
485. (C) Iran
486. (C) Pushkar
487. (D) Thailand
488. (B) Jataka Tales
489. (B) Grand sons
490. (A) 7 years
491. (C) Holi
492. (B) Angkorwat-Cambodia
493. (C) Harijans
494. (A) Christianity
495. (B) Vaayu
496. (B) Jains
497. (C) Vishnu
498. (D) Pilgrimage to Mecca (Hajj)
499. (A) Pope
500. (C) Kalki
501. (B) Parsis
502. (B) Christians
503. (A) Abu Bakr
504. (D) Ali
505. (A) Genesis
506. (A) Brahadeeswar Temple-Tanjore, TN
507. (C) Kaushalya
508. (B) Valmiki
509. (D) Gajapathy
510. (B) Tirupati
511. (B) 33 years
512. (C) Shintoism
513. (B) Cain & Abel
514. (D) Mohamed
515. (B) Ubu'l Kassim
516. (B) Vishnu
517. (C) Indonesia
518. (B) USA
519. (A) John
520. (B) Durga

521. (C) Obadiah
522. (B) Masjid
523. (C) Indra
524. (D) Golgotha
525. (C) Both of above
526. (B) Cardinals
527. (D) All of these
528. (B) Tirumala-Tirupati
529. (D) Holy war (Jihad)
530. (C) Bahaiism
531. (B) Siddhi
532. (A) USA
533. (B) 8th June 632 AD
534. (B) Menorah
535. (B) Indonesia
536. (B) Lao-Tse
537. (C) Jain
538. (B) Mirza Hussain Ali
539. (C) Medina
540. (B) Easter
541. (D) Bharata
542. (B) Nepal
543. (C) New York-USA
544. (B) Suddhodana-Maya
545. (C) Zen
546. (C) Shah Faizal Mosque-Pakistan
547. (D) St.John-The divine-New York
548. (A) Parsis
549. (D) All of these
550. (B) Jagannatha temple-Puri
551. (B) Abhay Charan de
552. (B) Tao Teh Ching
553. (B) Shintoism
554. (C) Atheism
555. (A) China
556. (D) March 21st
557. (D) 99
558. (B) Chapels
559. (C) Allahabad
560. (C) Universe